PRENTICE HALL MATHEMATICS

ALGEBRA 2

Chapter 13
Support File

Periodic Functions and Trigonometry

Prentice
Hall

Needham, Massachusetts
Upper Saddle River, New Jersey
Glenview, Illinois

ISBN: 0-13-063832-3

1 2 3 4 5 6 7 8 9 10   06 05 04 03 02

Chapter 13

Periodic Functions and Trigonometry

Practice 13-1

Exploring Periodic Data

Determine whether each function *is* or *is not* periodic. If it is, find
the period.

1.
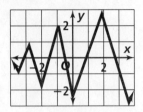

2.
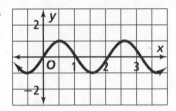

3.
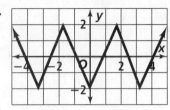

For each function, identify one cycle in two different ways. Then determine
the period of the function.

4.
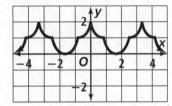

5.
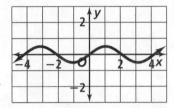

6.
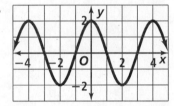

Find the period and amplitude of each periodic function.

7.
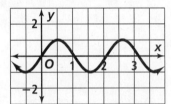

8.
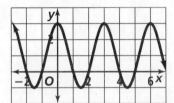

9.
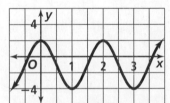

10.
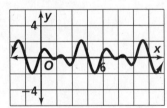

11.
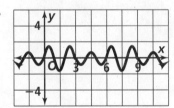

12.
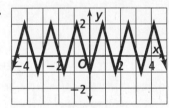

13.
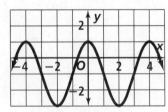

14.
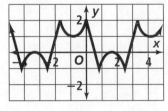

15.
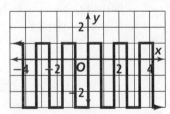

16.
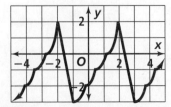

17.
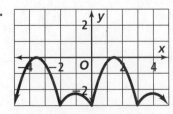

18.
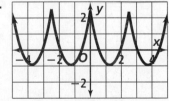

Practice 13-2

Sketch each angle in standard position.

1. 30° **2.** 60° **3.** 100° **4.** 135° **5.** 210°

6. 270° **7.** 330° **8.** −30° **9.** −90° **10.** −190°

11. −150° **12.** −330° **13.** −45° **14.** 315° **15.** −180°

16. 120° **17.** −120° **18.** 145° **19.** −145° **20.** −355°

Find the measure of an angle between 0° and 360° coterminal with each given angle.

21. −100° **22.** −60° **23.** −225° **24.** −145° **25.** 372°

26. −15° **27.** 482° **28.** 484° **29.** −20° **30.** 421°

31. 409° **32.** −38° **33.** 376° **34.** −210° **35.** 387°

36. 390° **37.** 660° **38.** 440° **39.** −170° **40.** 370°

41. −700° **42.** 458° **43.** 480° **44.** 406° **45.** −120°

46. 460° **47.** −222° **48.** −330° **49.** −127° **50.** 377°

Find the exact coordinates of the point where the terminal side of the given angle intersects the unit circle. Then find the decimal equivalents. Round your answers to the nearest hundredth.

51. 45° **52.** 225° **53.** −225° **54.** −45° **55.** 330°

56. −330° **57.** 150° **58.** −150° **59.** 300° **60.** −300°

61. 240° **62.** 120° **63.** −90° **64.** 360° **65.** 720°

66.
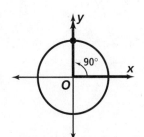

67.
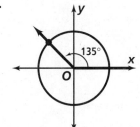

68.
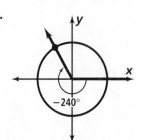

Find the measure of each angle in standard position.

69.
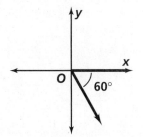

70.
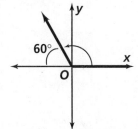

71.
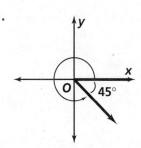

Practice 13-3

Write each measure in radians. Express your answer in terms of π.

1. 45°   **2.** 90°   **3.** 30°   **4.** 150°   **5.** 180°

6. 240°   **7.** 270°   **8.** 300°   **9.** 360°   **10.** 40°

11. 80°   **12.** 110°   **13.** 160°   **14.** 200°   **15.** 220°

Write each measure in degrees. Round your answer to the nearest degree, if necessary.

16. π **17.** 2π **18.** $\frac{5\pi}{6}$ **19.** $\frac{3\pi}{4}$ **20.** $\frac{3\pi}{2}$

21. $\frac{\pi}{6}$ **22.** $\frac{7\pi}{6}$ **23.** $\frac{11\pi}{6}$ **24.** $\frac{\pi}{3}$ **25.** $\frac{4\pi}{3}$

26. $\frac{5\pi}{4}$ **27.** $\frac{7\pi}{4}$ **28.** $\frac{2\pi}{3}$ **29.** $\frac{\pi}{9}$ **30.** $\frac{2\pi}{9}$

The measure θ of an angle in standard position is given. Find the exact values of cos θ and sin θ for each angle measure.

31. $\frac{\pi}{6}$ radians   **32.** $\frac{\pi}{3}$ radians   **33.** $-\frac{3\pi}{4}$ radians   **34.** $\frac{7\pi}{4}$ radians

35. $\frac{5\pi}{6}$ radians   **36.** $\frac{4\pi}{3}$ radians   **37.** $\frac{11\pi}{6}$ radians   **38.** $\frac{2\pi}{3}$ radians

Use each circle to find the length of the indicated arc. Round your answer to the nearest tenth.

39.
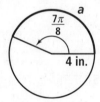

40.

41.
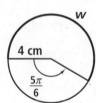

42.
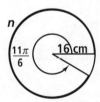

43.
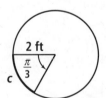

44.
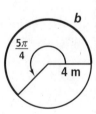

45. A pendulum swings through an angle of 1.8 radians. The distance the tip of the pendulum travels is 32 in. How long is the pendulum?

46. A 0.8 m pendulum swings through an angle of 1.5 radians. What distance does the tip of the pendulum travel?

Practice 13-4

Find the amplitude and period of each sine curve. Then write an equation for each curve.

1.
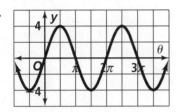

2.
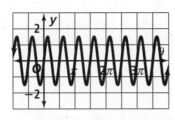

3.
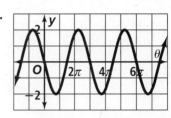

4.
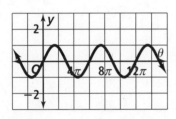

5.
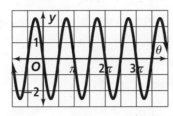

6.
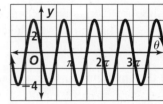

Sketch one cycle of each sine curve. Assume $a > 0$. Write an equation for each graph.

7. amplitude = 2; period = π

8. amplitude = 3; period = 2π

9. amplitude = 2; period = $\frac{\pi}{2}$

10. amplitude = 2; period = $\frac{\pi}{4}$

11. amplitude = 1.5; period = $\frac{\pi}{3}$

12. amplitude = 2.5; period = 2π

Sketch one cycle of the graph of each sine function.

13. $y = 2 \sin \theta$

14. $y = -2 \sin 4\theta$

15. $y = \sin 2\theta$

16. $y = 3 \sin \frac{\theta}{2}$

17. $y = -\sin 2\theta$

18. $y = -5 \sin 3\theta$

19. $y = -3 \sin 2\theta$

20. $y = 4 \sin 5\theta$

21. $y = -4 \sin \frac{\theta}{2}$

Use the graph at the right to find the value of $y = 0.3 \sin \theta$ for each value of θ.

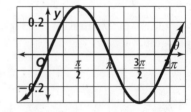

22. 6 radians

23. $\frac{\pi}{4}$ radians

24. $\frac{3\pi}{4}$ radians

25. $\frac{\pi}{2}$ radian

Use the graph at the right to find the value of $y = 0.3 \sin \theta$ for each value of θ.

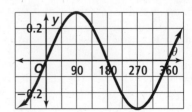

26. 160°

27. 135°

28. 270°

29. 225°

Practice 13-5

The Cosine Function

Sketch the graph of each function in the interval from 0 to 2π.

1. $y = \cos \theta$

2. $y = 2 \cos \pi\theta$

3. $y = 5 \cos \theta$

4. $y = -\cos \theta$

5. $y = -5 \cos \theta$

6. $y = \cos 2\pi\theta$

7. $y = -2 \cos 2\theta$

8. $y = 3 \cos 4\theta$

9. $y = \cos \frac{\theta}{2}$

10. $y = 3 \cos 8\theta$

11. $y = -4 \cos \pi\theta$

12. $y = 0.5 \cos \pi\theta$

13. $y = -\cos 2\theta$

14. $y = -3 \cos \frac{\pi}{2}\theta$

15. $y = 4 \cos \pi\theta$

16. Suppose 12 in. waves occur every 5 s. Write an equation using a cosine function that models the height of a water particle as it moves from crest to crest.

Write the equation of a cosine function for each graph.

17.

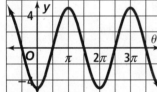

18.

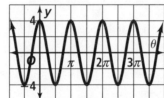

19.

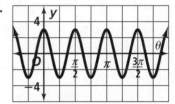

Find the period and amplitude of each cosine function. Identify where the maximum value, minimum value, and zeros occur in the interval from 0 to 2π.

20.

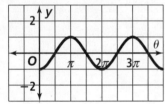

21.

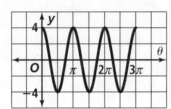

22.

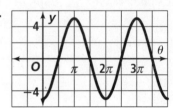

Solve each equation in the interval from 0 to 2π. Round to the nearest hundredth.

23. $2 \cos 3\theta = 1.5$

24. $\cot \frac{t}{3} = 1$

25. $1.5 \cos \pi\theta = -1.5$

26. $3 \cos \frac{\pi}{5} \theta = 2$

27. $3 \cos t = 2$

28. $0.5 \cos \frac{\theta}{2} = 0.5$

29. $4 \cos \frac{\pi}{4} \theta = -2$

30. $3 \cos \frac{\theta}{4} = 1.5$

31. $3 \cos \theta = -3$

Write a cosine function for each description. Assume that $a > 0$.

32. amplitude $= 2\pi$, period $= 1$

33. amplitude $= \frac{1}{2}$, period $= \pi$

Practice 13-6

Identify the period and tell where the asymptotes occur, in the interval from
0 to 2π, for each function.

1. $y = \tan \theta$

2. $y = 2 \tan \dfrac{\theta}{2}$

3. $y = 3 \tan \dfrac{\theta}{4}$

4. $y = 4 \tan 2\theta$

5. $y = -\tan \dfrac{\pi}{2} \theta$

6. $y = -2 \tan \pi\theta$

7. $y = -3 \tan 2\theta$

8. $y = -4 \tan \theta$

9. $y = 0.5 \tan \pi\theta$

Sketch two cycles of the graph of each function.

10. $y = \tan \theta$

11. $y = 2 \tan \theta$

12. $y = -\tan \theta$

13. $y = -2 \tan \theta$

14. $y = -0.5 \tan 2\theta$

15. $y = 3 \tan \theta$

16. $y = -3 \tan 2\theta$

17. $y = 5 \tan \dfrac{\pi}{2} \theta$

18. $y = 2 \tan 3\theta$

19. $y = 0.5 \tan 2\theta$

20. $y = -2.5 \tan \dfrac{\pi}{2} \theta$

21. $y = -5 \tan 2\pi\theta$

22. $y = -2 \tan 4\theta$

23. $y = -0.25 \tan 3\theta$

24. $y = -4 \tan 4\pi\theta$

25. $y = -2.25 \tan \theta$

26. $y = -0.25 \tan \dfrac{\pi}{3} \theta$

27. $y = 0.75 \tan 4\theta$

Identify the period of each tangent function.

28.

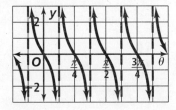

29.

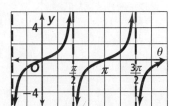

30.

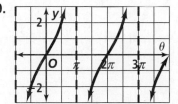

Use the graph of $y = \tan \theta$ to find each value. If the tangent is undefined at
that point, write *undefined*.

31. $\tan \dfrac{\pi}{2}$

32. $\tan \left(-\dfrac{3\pi}{4} \right)$

33. $\tan \left(-\dfrac{\pi}{4} \right)$

34. $\tan \dfrac{3\pi}{2}$

Using your graphing calculator, graph each function on the interval $0° < x < 470°$
and $-300 < y < 300$. Evaluate the function at $x = 45°, 90°,$ and $135°$.

35. $y = 200 \tan x$

36. $y = -75 \tan \left(\dfrac{1}{4}x \right)$

37. $y = -50 \tan x$

Name _____ Class _____ Date _____

Practice 13-7

Graph each function in the interval from 0 to 2π.

1. $y = -\sin\left(x + \dfrac{\pi}{2}\right)$

2. $y = 3\sin\left(x - \dfrac{\pi}{4}\right) + 2$

3. $y = \cos\dfrac{1}{2}x + 1$

4. $y = 3\cos(x - 2)$

5. $y = \sin 3(x - \pi)$

6. $y = \cos(x + 4)$

7. $y = \cos x + 3$

8. $y = -2\sin x + 1$

9. $y = -\cos 2\left(x + \dfrac{\pi}{4}\right)$

10. $y = \dfrac{1}{2}\cos x + 3$

11. $y = \sin\dfrac{1}{2}(x + \pi)$

12. $y = \cos\left(x + \dfrac{\pi}{6}\right)$

13. $y = -2\cos x + 3$

14. $y = \sin 2x + 1$

15. $y = \sin 2\left(x - \dfrac{\pi}{3}\right)$

Write an equation for each translation.

16. $y = \sin x$, 2 units down

17. $y = \cos x$, π units left

18. $y = \cos x$, $\dfrac{\pi}{4}$ units up

19. $y = \sin x$, 3.2 units to the right

Find the amplitude and period of each function. Describe any phase shift and vertical shift in the graph.

20. $y = 3\cos x + 2$

21. $y = -2\sin\left(x + \dfrac{\pi}{2}\right)$

22. $y = \cos 2x + 1$

23. $y = -\sin\left(x - \dfrac{\pi}{3}\right)$

24. $y = \dfrac{1}{2}\cos x - 3$

25. $y = \cos\dfrac{1}{2}x - 2$

Use the function $f(x)$ at the right. Graph each translation.

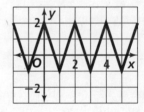

26. $f(x) + 3$

27. $f(x + 1)$

28. $f(x) - 5$

29. $f(x + 3)$

30. $f(x + 2) - 1$

31. $f(x) - 4$

What is the value of h in each translation? Describe each phase shift (use a phrase like *3 units to the left*).

32. $g(x) = f(x + 2)$

33. $g(x) = f(x - 1)$

34. $h(t) = f(t + 1.5)$

35. $f(x) = g(x - 1)$

36. $y = \cos\left(x - \dfrac{\pi}{2}\right)$

37. $y = \cos(x + \pi)$

Practice 13-8

Evaluate each expression. Each angle is given in radians. Round to the nearest thousandth, if necessary.

1. $\cot 4$

2. $\csc \frac{\pi}{6}$

3. $\csc(-2)$

4. $\sec \pi$

5. $\cot(-\pi)$

6. $\sec(-3.5)$

7. $\cot \frac{\pi}{3}$

8. $\sec 1.5$

9. $\csc(-1.5)$

10. $\cot \pi$

11. $\sec 3$

12. $\csc \frac{\pi}{4}$

Evaluate each expression. Write your answer in exact form. If appropriate, also state it as a decimal rounded to the nearest hundredth. If the expression is undefined, write *undefined*.

13. $\sec 45°$

14. $\cot 180°$

15. $\sec 30°$

16. $\csc 30°$

17. $\cot(-180°)$

18. $\csc(-45°)$

19. $\csc 180°$

20. $\cot 45°$

21. $\sec 90°$

22. $\sec(-30°)$

23. $\csc(-60°)$

24. $\sec 60°$

25. Suppose $\tan \theta = \frac{6}{9}$. Find $\cot \theta$

26. Suppose $\sin \theta = \frac{2}{5}$. Find $\csc \theta$

27. Suppose $\cos \theta = \frac{14}{20}$. Find $\sec \theta$

28. Suppose $\tan \theta = -\frac{2}{3}$. Find $\cot \theta$

Graph each function in the interval from 0 to 2π.

29. $y = \cot 2\theta$

30. $y = -\cot \frac{1}{2}\theta$

31. $y = \sec\left(\theta - \frac{\pi}{2}\right)$

32. $y = \csc 2\theta + 1$

33. $y = -\csc 3\theta$

34. $y = \sec \theta + 2$

35. $y = \cot(\theta + \pi)$

36. $y = \sec \frac{1}{4}\theta$

37. $y = \csc \theta - 1$

Use the graph of the appropriate reciprocal trigonometric function to find each value. Round to the nearest thousandth, if necessary.

38. $\cot 30°$

39. $\csc 180°$

40. $\cot 70°$

41. $\sec 100°$

42. $\sec 50°$

43. $\csc 100°$

44. $\cot 20°$

45. $\sec 120°$

46. A fire truck is parked on the shoulder of a freeway next to a long wall. The red light on the top of the truck rotates through one complete revolution every 2 seconds. The function $y = 10 \sec \pi t$ models the length of the beam in feet to a point on the wall in terms of time t.

   a. Graph the function.

   b. Find the length at time 1.75 seconds

   c. Find the length at time 2 seconds.

Reteaching 13-1

OBJECTIVE: Recognizing periodic graphs and their features	**MATERIALS:** Yellow, pink, and green highlighting markers

- The Graph of a *periodic function* shows a repeating pattern. The distance from one point on the graph to the point where the pattern begins repeating is called the *period*.

- To find the amplitude, use $A = \frac{1}{2}$ (maximum value – minimum value).

Example

Determine if the graph represents a periodic function. If it is periodic, calculate the period and amplitude of the function.

The repeating pattern determines that the function is periodic.

Draw a vertical line on the graph with the yellow marker. Draw another vertical line at the point where the graph completes one cycle of the pattern.

Draw a horizontal line with a green marker from the *y*-axis to the highest points on the graph.

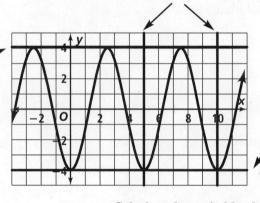

Draw a horizontal line with the pink marker from the *y*-axis to the lowest points on the graph.

Period = 10 − 5 = 5   ⟵ **Calculate the period by determining the distance from one yellow line to the other.**

Amplitude = $\frac{1}{2}(4 - (-4)) = \frac{1}{2}(8) = 4$ ⟵ **Calculate the amplitude using the formula with the maximum being the *y*-value at the green marker and the minimum value the *y*-value at the pink marker.**

Exercises

For each graph of a periodic function, calculate the period and amplitude of the function.

1.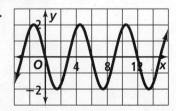

2.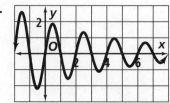

3.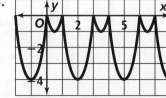

Reteaching 13-2

Angles and the Unit Circle

OBJECTIVE: Finding the coordinates of points on the unit circle	**MATERIALS:** Ruler, protractor, compass, and calculator

Example

Find the coordinates of the point where the terminal side of a 315° angle intersects the unit circle.

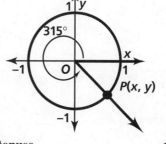

Step 1: Use a compass to draw a unit circle. Use a protractor to sketch the angle. Have the terminal side of the angle intersect the circle.

Step 2: Since the terminal side is in the fourth quadrant, x is positive and y is negative.

Step 3: Use a ruler to draw the horizontal leg of the right triangle. The terminal side of the angle is its hypotenuse. The negative y-axis is the other leg.

Step 4: Since $360 - 315 = 45$, you can label the acute angles of the triangle as 45°. Use properties of special right triangles. The length of the hypotenuse is $\sqrt{2}$ times the length of a leg. Label each leg s.

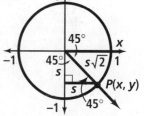

hypotenuse = 1

$$s\sqrt{2} = 1$$

$$s = \frac{1}{\sqrt{2}}$$

$$s = \frac{\sqrt{2}}{2}$$

each leg $= \dfrac{\sqrt{2}}{2}$

Step 5: The unit circle has a radius of 1 unit.

Substitute $s\sqrt{2}$ for the length of the hypotenuse.

Divide both sides by $\sqrt{2}$.

Rationalize the denominator by multiplying the fraction by $\dfrac{\sqrt{2}}{\sqrt{2}}$.

The coordinates of the point of intersection are $\left(\dfrac{\sqrt{2}}{2}, -\dfrac{\sqrt{2}}{2}\right)$.

Exercises

Find the coordinates of the point where the terminal side of each angle intersects the unit circle.

1. $-150°$ **2.** $30°$ **3.** $-330°$ **4.** $-45°$ **5.** $120°$ **6.** $225°$

Reteaching 13-3

OBJECTIVE: Using radian measure for angles   **MATERIALS:** None

- When converting radians to degrees or degrees to radians, use the proportion
$\dfrac{\text{degree measure}}{360} = \dfrac{\text{radian measure}}{2\pi}$.

Example

Write the measure of 225° in radians.

$\dfrac{225}{360} = \dfrac{x}{2\pi}$ ⟵ **Substitute 225 for degree measure and a variable for radian measure.**

$360x = 450\pi$ ⟵ **Cross multiply.**

$x = \dfrac{450\pi}{360}$ ⟵ **Divide both sides by 360.**

$x = \dfrac{5\pi}{4}$ ⟵ **Simplify.**

$x \approx 3.93$ ⟵ **Use a calculator.**

$\dfrac{\theta}{360} = \dfrac{\frac{5}{4}\pi}{2\pi}$ ⟵ **Check by substituting the radians into the proportion and solving for degrees.**

$\dfrac{\theta}{360} = \dfrac{\frac{5}{4}\cancel{\pi}}{2\cancel{\pi}}$ ⟵ **Cancel π since it is in the numerator and denominator.**

$2\theta = 450$ ⟵ **Cross multiply.**

$\theta = 225$ ⟵ **Divide both sides by 2. This gives the degree measure.**

An angle of 225° measures about 3.93 radians.

Exercises

Write each measure in radians and check.

1. 20°   **2.** 150°   **3.** 45°

4. −110°   **5.** 315°   **6.** 320°

Write each measure in degrees and check.

7. $-\dfrac{3\pi}{2}$ **8.** $\dfrac{5\pi}{3}$ **9.** $\dfrac{\pi}{12}$

10. $\dfrac{8\pi}{5}$ **11.** $-\dfrac{7\pi}{6}$ **12.** $\dfrac{9\pi}{2}$

Reteaching 13-4

The Sine Function

| **OBJECTIVE:** Graphing sine curves | **MATERIALS:** Graph paper, colored pencils, and string |

Example

Graph at least two cycles of the function $y = 2 \sin \frac{1}{2}\theta$.

$|a| = 2$	**Step 1:** Find the amplitude.
$b = \frac{1}{2}$	Find the number of cycles in the interval from 0 to 2π.
$\frac{2\pi}{b} = \frac{2\pi}{\frac{1}{2}}$	Find the period of the curve.
$= 4\pi$	

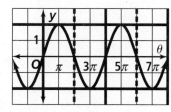

Step 2: Draw a horizontal and vertical axis. Label $\pi, 2\pi, 3\pi \ldots, 8\pi$. Draw a red solid vertical line at $0, 4\pi$, and 8π to denote the end of each cycle. Draw a blue dotted vertical line at 2π and 6π to denote one-half cycle. Draw a green solid horizontal line at $y = 2$ and $y = -2$ to denote the amplitude.

Step 3: Use string to form the graph. Then draw the graph.

Exercises

Graph each function.

1. $y = \sin \frac{1}{2}\theta$

2. $y = 2 \sin 3\theta$

3. $y = 5 \sin \theta$

4. $y = 2 \sin 2\theta$

5. $y = \sin \frac{1}{3}\theta$

6. $y = \frac{1}{2} \sin \theta$

7. $y = -2 \sin \frac{1}{2}\theta$

8. $y = -\sin 3\theta$

9. $y = -\frac{1}{4} \sin \theta$

Reteaching 13-5

OBJECTIVE: Graphing cosine curves   **MATERIALS:** None

• The basic equation for a cosine function is $y = a \cos b\theta$. The amplitude
   is $|a|$ and the period is $\frac{2\pi}{b}$.

Example

Identify the amplitude and period for the function
$y = 4 \cos 2\pi\theta$. Graph the function.

$\qquad y = 4 \cos 2\pi\theta$

$\qquad |a| = |4| = 4$ ⟵   **Find the amplitude of the function.**

$\qquad \dfrac{2\pi}{b} = \dfrac{2\pi}{2\pi} = 1$ ⟵   **Calculate the period of the function.**

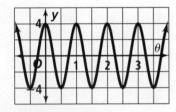   ⟵   **Since the amplitude is 4, start the graph at (0, 4).**
Complete one cycle between 0 and 1 since the period is 1.

Exercises

Identify the amplitude and period. Graph each function.

1. $y = \frac{1}{2} \cos 2\theta$

2. $y = 3 \cos \frac{1}{2}\theta$

3. $y = \cos 3\theta$

4. $y = \frac{1}{4} \cos \pi\theta$

5. $y = -2 \cos \frac{1}{2}\theta$

6. $y = 2 \cos 6\pi\theta$

7. $y = -2 \cos \theta$

8. $y = \cos \frac{1}{5}\theta$

9. $y = 2 \cos 2\theta$

Reteaching 13-6

The Tangent Function

OBJECTIVE: Graphing tangent curves	MATERIALS: None

The tangent function is a discontinuous periodic function. Its equation in standard form is $y = \tan b\theta$. For the tangent function, b, represents the number of cycles from 0 to π, and its period is $\frac{\pi}{b}$. One cycle occurs in the interval from $-\frac{\pi}{2b}$ to $\frac{\pi}{2b}$, and vertical asymptotes occur at the end of each cycle.

Example

Graph the function $y = 3 \tan \pi\theta$.

$\frac{\pi}{b} = \frac{\pi}{\pi} = 1$ ⟵ **Calculate the period of the function. One cycle occurs in the interval $-\frac{1}{2}$ to $\frac{1}{2}$.**

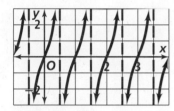 ⟵ **Because the period is 1, asymptotes occur every 1 unit— at $\ldots, -\frac{1}{2}, \frac{1}{2}, \frac{3}{2}, \frac{5}{2}, \frac{7}{2}, \ldots$.**

Plot three points in each cycle. Sketch the curve.

Exercises

Identify the period and tell where the asymptotes occur between 0 and 2π. Graph each function.

1. $y = 3 \tan 2\theta$

2. $y = -2 \tan \frac{1}{2}\theta$

3. $y = -2 \tan \theta$

4. $y = 2 \tan 2\theta$

5. $y = -\tan \frac{\pi}{2}\theta$

6. $y = \frac{1}{2} \tan \theta$

7. $y = \tan 3\theta$

8. $y = -2 \tan \frac{1}{2}\pi\theta$

9. $y = 2 \tan \frac{\pi}{4}\theta$

Reteaching 13-7

Translating Sine and Cosine Functions

OBJECTIVE: Graphing translations of trigonometric curves

MATERIALS: None

A horizontal translation of a periodic function is a phase shift.
When $g(x) = f(x-h)$, the value of h is the amount of the shift left or right.
If $h > 0$, the shift is to the right. If $h < 0$, the shift is to the left.

A vertical translation can occur as well. When $g(x) = f(x) + k$, the value
of k is the amount of the shift up or down. If $k > 0$, the shift is up. If $k < 0$,
the shift is down.

Example

Sketch the graph of $y = 2 \sin 3\left(x - \frac{\pi}{3}\right) + 1$ in the interval from 0 to 2π.

Since $a = 2$ and $b = 3$, the graph is a translation of $y = 2 \sin 3x$.

Step 1: **Sketch one cycle of $y = 2 \sin 3x$.**
Use five points in the pattern
zero–max–zero–min–zero.

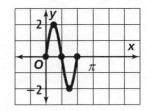

Step 2: **Since $h = \frac{\pi}{3}$ and $k = 1$, translate**
the graph $\frac{\pi}{3}$ units to the right and 1 unit up.
Extend the periodic pattern throughout
the interval from 0 to 2π. Sketch the graph.

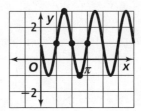

Exercises

Sketch each graph in the interval from 0 to 2π.

1. $y = \cos 3\left(x + \frac{\pi}{2}\right)$

2. $y = -2 \sin \frac{1}{2}x - 1$

3. $y = -2 \cos (x + \pi) - 2$

4. $y = \frac{1}{2} \sin 2(x - 2)$

5. $y = -\sin 2x + 3$

6. $y = \frac{1}{2} \cos \left(x - \frac{\pi}{3}\right)$

7. $y = \sin 3x + \frac{1}{2}$

8. $y = -2 \cos \frac{1}{2}(x + \pi)$

9. $y = 2 \cos \frac{\pi}{4}x + 2.5$

Reteaching 13-8

OBJECTIVE: Graphing reciprocal trigonometric functions

MATERIALS: None

The cosecant (csc), secant (sec), and cotangent (cot) functions are defined as reciprocals of the sine (sin), cosine (cos), and tangent (tan) functions, respectively. Their domains include all real numbers except those that make a denominator zero.

$$\csc \theta = \frac{1}{\sin \theta} \qquad \sec \theta = \frac{1}{\cos \theta} \qquad \cot \theta = \frac{1}{\tan \theta}$$

Example

Sketch the graph of $y = \cos \theta$ and $y = \sec \theta$ in the interval from 0 to 2π.

Step 1: Make a table of values. The graph of $y = \sec \theta$ has asymptotes where $\cos \theta$ is equal to zero.

θ	0	$\frac{\pi}{4}$	$\frac{\pi}{2}$	$\frac{3\pi}{4}$	π	$\frac{5\pi}{4}$	$\frac{3\pi}{2}$	$\frac{7\pi}{4}$	2π
$\cos \theta$	1	0.71	0	−0.71	−1	−0.71	0	0.71	1
$\sec \theta$	1	1.41	—	−1.41	−1	−1.41	—	1.41	1

Step 2: Plot the points and sketch the graphs.

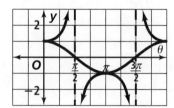

Exercises

Sketch each graph in the interval from 0 to 2π.

1. $y = \cot 3\theta$

2. $y = -2 \sec \frac{1}{2}\theta$

3. $y = -2 \csc (\theta + \pi) - 2$

4. $y = \frac{1}{2} \csc 2(\theta - 2)$

5. $y = -\sec 2\theta$

6. $y = \frac{1}{2} \cot \left(\theta - \frac{\pi}{2}\right)$

7. $y = \cot 3\theta + \frac{1}{2}$

8. $y = -2 \csc \frac{1}{2}\theta$

9. $y = 2 \cot \frac{\pi}{4}\theta$

Enrichment 13-1

Lesson on Excellence

Have you ever wondered what the benefit of homework is? Maybe a quote
by a famous philosopher will sum it up.

We are what we repeatedly do. Excellence, then, is not an act, but a habit.

To find out who said this quote, complete the puzzle below.

**Find the indicated period or amplitude then match the given letter to the
numbered line.**

1.

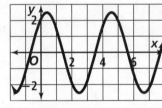

R = period ÷ 4

2.

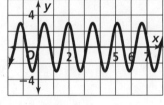

E = amplitude × 3

3.

L = period × 2

4.

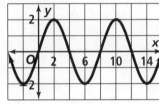

S = amplitude × 2

5.

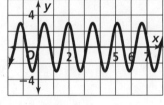

T = amplitude × 7

6.

A = period ÷ 2

7.

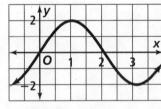

T = amplitude × 2

8.

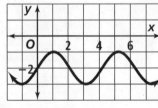

O = amplitude × 6

9.

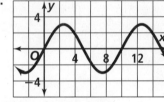

I = amplitude

___ ___ ___ ___ ___ ___ ___ ___ ___
 1   2   3   4   5   6   7   8   9

Enrichment 13-2

•••
Nautical Miles

Recall that $1°$ is $\frac{1}{360}$ of a full rotation. A degree itself can be broken down further. If we divide $1°$ into 60 equal parts, each one of the parts is called 1 minute, denoted $1'$. One minute is $\frac{1}{60}$ of a degree; there are 60 minutes in every degree.

If a central angle with its vertex at the center of the earth has a measure of $1'$, then the arc on the surface of the earth that is cut off by this angle has a measure of 1 nautical mile.

For the following problems, assume that the radius of the earth is 4000 miles.

1. Find the number of regular (statute) miles in 1 nautical mile to the nearest hundredth of a mile.

2. If two ships are 20 nautical miles apart on the ocean, how may statute miles apart are they? Use the result from Exercise 1 in your calculation.

3. Two islands are in the ocean. If the central angle with vertex at the center of the earth that has these two islands on either side of it measures $12'$, how many statute miles apart are they? Use the result from Exercise 1 in your calculation.

4. Los Angeles and San Francisco are approximately 450 miles apart on the surface of the earth. Find the measure of the central angle with its vertex at the center of the earth that has Los Angeles on one side and San Francisco on the other side.

5. Los Angeles and New York City are approximately 2500 miles apart on the surface of the earth. Find the measure of the central angle with its vertex at the center of the earth that has Los Angeles on one side and New York City on the other side.

Enrichment 13-3

· ·

Conversion Formulas

Radian measure results in an easy-to-remember formula for computing the length of an arc of a circle subtended by a given angle. Suppose we are given two concentric circles, one of radius r and one of radius 1, and a central angle A.

Let s denote the length of the arc subtended by $\angle A$ in the circle of radius 1. Let S denote the length of the arc subtended by $\angle A$ in the circle of radius r.

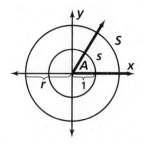

1. Write an equation involving the ratios of the arc lengths to the radii of the circles.

2. If A represents the measure of $\angle A$ in radians, express A in terms of s.

3. Express A in terms of S and r.

4. Use your results to find S in terms of r and A.

5. In a circle of radius 3, find the length of the arc subtended by a central angle of 60°.

6. Recall that there are 360° or 2π radians in a circle. If A represents the number of radians and D represents the number of degree in $\angle A$, write a proportion that can be used to convert between degrees and radians.

7. Derive a formula for the length of the arc S subtended by $\angle A$ in terms of D.

8. What is the length of the arc S subtended by an angle of V revolutions along a circle of radius r?

9. Revolutions are often used to express rates of angular rotation. For example, the rate of angular rotation of a long-playing record is $33\frac{1}{3}$ rpm. Express this rate in radians per second.

Enrichment 13-4

• •

Word Ladders

How can you go from degrees to radians? One way is with a word ladder.
A word ladder is a sequence of words in which only one letter in each word
changes. To find a word ladder from *deg* to *rad,* find the sine of each of the
following angles.

Associated with each exercise is a pair of letters. Fill in the word ladder by
placing the first letter of the pair on the line numbered the same as the
tenths digit of the answer and the second letter on the line numbered the same as the
hundredths digit. Fill in only one letter at a time.

D	E	G
___	___	___
4	5	3
___	___	___
6	5	2
___	___	___
6	7	2
___	___	___
1	7	8
___	___	___
1	9	3
___	___	___
0	9	8
R	A	D

1. DG $\sin 25° = $ _____

2. OG $\sin 36° = $ _____

3. GG $\sin 19° = $ _____

4. BA $\sin 11° = $ _____

5. RG $\sin 5° = $ _____

6. AE $\sin 76° = $ _____

7. LO $\sin 41° = $ _____

8. LB $\sin 38° = $ _____

9. GE $\sin 22° = $ _____

Enrichment 13-5

· ·

Calculating Trigonometric Functions

How are values of trigonometric functions of other angles, such as 26°, calculated? One way is to construct a right triangle in which one of the angles is 26°. Then measure the sides and perform the necessary arithmetic. This approach has its drawbacks. First, accuracy is limited to the accuracy with which the angles and sides can be measured. Second, it is time-consuming.

Another way, which can be carried out to any degree of accuracy, involves the use of certain polynomials. For example, the following three polynomials can be used to approximate the sine of an angle measured in radians.

$$S_3(x) = x - \frac{x^3}{6} \qquad S_5(x) = x - \frac{x^3}{6} + \frac{x^5}{120} \qquad S_7(x) = x - \frac{x^3}{6} + \frac{x^5}{120} - \frac{x^7}{5040}$$

By using a calculator to complete the following table, you can see how these polynomials approximate the sine function to various degrees of accuracy.

Let D be the number of degrees in the angle. Let x be the *radian* measure of $\angle D$. Compute the value of each polynomial to six decimal places using x. Then compute $\sin x$ to six decimal places.

	D	x	$S_3(x)$	$S_5(x)$	$S_7(x)$	$\sin x$
1.	5°	$\frac{\pi}{36}$	0.087156			
2.	11°					
3.	26°					
4.	37°					

5. Discuss the results of the table.

These three polynomials can be used to approximate the cosine of any angle:

$$C_2(x) = 1 - \frac{x^2}{2} \qquad C_4(x) = 1 - \frac{x^2}{2} + \frac{x^4}{24} \qquad C_6(x) = 1 - \frac{x^2}{2} + \frac{x^4}{24} - \frac{x^6}{720}$$

Fill in the following table as done for Exercises 1–4.

	D	x	$C_2(x)$	$C_4(x)$	$C_6(x)$	$\cos x$
6.	5°	$\frac{\pi}{36}$	0.996192			
7.	11°					
8.	26°					
9.	37°					

10. Discuss the results of the table.

Enrichment 13-6

•••

Even and Odd Functions

Functions which meet certain criteria are classified as *even* functions or *odd* functions.

An *even* function is a function for which $f(-x) = f(x)$ for all x in the domain of f.

1. If a function is even, then every time the point (a, b) is on the graph, so is the point _____.

An *odd* function is a function for which $f(-x) = -f(x)$ for all x in the domain of f.

2. If a function is odd, then every time the point (a, b) is on the graph, so is the point _____.

Let's explore even and odd functions in relation to the trigonometric functions. We can use the unit circle to do this.

3. $\sin 30° = $ _____ $\sin (-30°) = $ _____

   $\sin 45° = $ _____ $\sin (-45°) = $ _____

   $\sin 60° = $ _____ $\sin (-60°) = $ _____

   Is the sine function even or odd? How do you know?

4. $\cos 30° = $ _____ $\cos (-30°) = $ _____

   $\cos 45° = $ _____ $\cos (-45°) = $ _____

   $\cos 60° = $ _____ $\cos (-60°) = $ _____

   Is the cosine function even or odd? How do you know?

The results of Exercises 1 and 2 show that even and odd functions can be described in terms of symmetry. Even functions are symmetric with respect to the y-axis and odd functions are symmetric with respect to the origin.

5. Examine the graph of $y = \sin x$. What special kind of symmetry does the graph appear to have? From your answer, is the function even or odd?

6. Examine the graph of $y = \cos x$. What special kind of symmetry does the graph appear to have? From your answer, is the function even or odd?

7. Examine the graph of $y = \tan x$. What special kind of symmetry does the graph appear to have? From your answer, is the function even or odd?

Enrichment 13-7

Ferris Wheel

The first Ferris Wheel was designed and built by an American engineer named George W. G. Ferris in 1893. It had 36 cars that each held 40 passengers. The diameter of the wheel was 250 feet. The top of the wheel was 264 feet above the ground and it took 20 minutes to complete one revolution.

Trigonometric functions can be used to model the position of a rider on a ferris wheel. We will find the equation to model this situation.

Begin by making a table of values. Let y represent the height of the rider above the ground x minutes into the ride.

x	y
0	
5	
10	
15	
20	

1. When $x = 0$ or 20, the rider is at the start of the ride.
   Find the appropriate value of y and place it in the table.

2. When $x = 10$, the rider is at the top of the wheel.
   Find the appropriate value of y and place it in the table.

3. When $x = 5$ or 15, the rider is even with the center of the wheel.
   Find the appropriate value of y and place it in the table.

Plot the ordered pairs on the graph to the right and connect them with a smooth curve. The shape of the curve matches that of a cosine curve. Therefore, the equation of the curve is of the form $y = a \cos b(x - h) + k$, where $|a|$ = amplitide, $\frac{2\pi}{b}$ = period (when x is in radians, and $b > 0$), h = phase shift, and k = vertical shift.

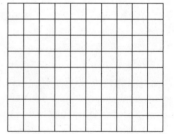

4. Find the amplitude.

5. Find the period. What value for b produces this period?

6. Using the results of Exercises 4 and 5 and choosing $a > 0$, write an equation of the form $y = a \cos bx$.

7. Find the values of h and k by comparing the graph of the equation found in Exercise 6 with the plot of the data.

8. Write an equation that models the height of the rider at any time x during the ride.

Enrichment 13-8

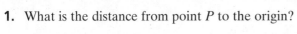

The Trigonometric Form of the Pythagorean Theorem

The unit circle is the circle whose center is the origin and whose radius is 1. Suppose the initial side of a central angle A is the x-axis. Let the terminal side of $\angle A$ intersect the unit circle at the point $P(x, y)$.

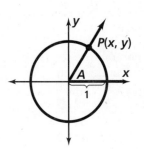

1. What is the distance from point P to the origin?

2. What are the values of $\sin A$ and $\cos A$ in terms of x and y?

3. What are the coordinates of point P in terms of $\angle A$?

4. Use the coordinates of P from Exercise 3 to write an equation expressing the distance from P to the origin.

5. Simplify your equation.

6. The result, usually written as $\sin^2 A + \cos^2 A = 1$, is known as the trigonometric form of the Pythagorean theorem. Solve the equation for $\cos A$ in terms of $\sin A$.

7. Express $\tan A$ in terms of $\sin A$ and $\cos A$.

8. How could you express $\tan A$ in terms of $\sin A$ only?

9. How could you express $\cot A$ in terms of $\sin A$ only?

As you can see, the trigonometric form of the Pythagorean theorem allows you to express any one function in terms of the others. Use the trigonometric form of the Pythagorean theorem to express each of the following functions as indicated.

10. $\sin A$ in terms of $\cos A$

11. $\cos A$ in terms of $\csc A$

12. $\tan A$ in terms of $\cos A$

Chapter 13 Project: The Wave of the Future

Beginning the Chapter Project

The ebb and flow of the ocean tides contain tremendous amounts of energy. For centuries this energy has been used to run tidal mills. In the last few decades, utility companies have explored ways to use this energy to generate electricity.

The tides vary greatly, but in predictable, repetitive ways that can be utilized. Tides are periodic, as are the functions in Chapter 13. To determine where a tidal power plant might be feasible, accurate predictions of the tides are essential.

In this project, you will consider how tides are modeled and how the periodic nature of tides creates special problems in the design of tidal power plants. Then you will summarize what you have learned and discuss whether you think tidal power plants will be a practical source of electricity in the future.

List of Materials

- Calculator
- Graph paper

Activities

Activity 1: Estimating
You can use a periodic function to approximate the cycle of tides. Every day at many locations around the world, people record the height of the tide above a level called *mean low water*. The following table shows possible data at two such locations. Estimate the period and amplitude of the function that models the tidal cycle at each location.

Location 1		Location 2	
Time	**Tide Height (ft)**	**Time**	**Tide Height (ft)**
11:30 A.M.	0.6	4:46 P.M.	−2.4
5:42 P.M.	4.8	10:59 P.M.	3.3
11:55 P.M.	0.6	5:11 A.M.	−2.4
6:07 A.M.	4.8	11:24 A.M.	3.3

Chapter 13 Project (continued)

Activity 2: Modeling

The range of the tides is affected by the relative positions of the sun and the moon. During the new moon and full moon, the highest high tides and the lowest low tides occur. During the first and third quarters of the lunar month, the lowest high tides and highest low tides occur. Throughout the month, the tidal range gradually increases and decreases between the minimum and maximum values of the range.

- Sketch a graph of a tidal range as a function of time, showing that you think the shape of a tidal cycle might look for one month. On your graph, indicate where you think each phase of the moon occurs.

- Research how the phases of the moon and the forces that control the tides are related. Include an illustration with your explanation.

Activity 3: Researching

To harness tidal power, a dam is built across the narrow neck of a bay where there is a large difference between high and low tide. Power is generated by both the incoming and outgoing tides as water flows through the dam. However, near the times of high and low tide, other sources of energy must be used to supplement tidal power.

- How does the periodic nature of tides explain why tidal power is not a steady source of energy?

- Determine in what parts of the world it is practical to harness tidal power.

- How do utility companies that use tidal power provide energy when their customers need it?

Finishing the Project

The answers to the activities should help you complete your project. Write a brief essay describing how the tides can be harnessed to create electrical power. Discuss the advantages and disadvantages of tidal power. Based on your research and analysis, do you think tidal power plants are practical sources of electricity for the future? Support your conclusions.

Reflect and Revise

Find someone in your class who reached a different conclusion about tidal power than you did. Read each other's essays. Discuss your differences of opinion. Have you changed your mind about your conclusions? If necessary, do further research and revise your paper.

Extending the Project

Research other factors that affect the cycle of tides such as the changing distances of the moon and sun from Earth. Describe these factors in terms of periodic functions, if possible.

 **Take it to the NET**

Visit PHSchool.com for information and links you might find helpful as you complete your project.

Chapter Project Manager

••

Chapter 13: The Wave of the Future

Getting Started

Read the project. As you work on the project, you need a calculator, materials on which you can record your calculations, and material to make accurate and attractive graphs. Keep all of your work for the project in a folder.

Checklist

☐ Activity 1: estimating period and amplitude

☐ Activity 2: graphing relationships between the moon and tides

☐ Activity 3: researching tidal power

☐ essay

Suggestions

☐ Use the fact that the amplitude is one half of the difference between the maximum and minimum.

☐ Show that the tidal range is greatest when the difference is at a maximum.

☐ Call your community's electric power company and use the Internet.

☐ In what professions would you find people whose work is directly affected by the motion of the tides? How would the graphs and charts you created for this project be helpful to these people?

Scoring Rubric

3 Calculations are correct. The graph is neat, accurate, and clearly shows the relationship between the variables. Scales are appropriate for the graph. Research is thorough and explanations are well thought out.

2 Calculations are mostly correct with some minor errors. The graph is neat and mostly accurate with minor errors in scale. Research is not thorough and explanations are not well thought out.

1 Calculations contain both minor and major errors. The graph is not accurate. Research and explanations are not adequate.

0 Major elements of the project are incomplete or missing.

Your Evaluation of Project Evaluate your work, based on the *Scoring Rubric.*

Teacher's Evaluation of Project

Chapter Project Teacher Notes

• •

Chapter 13: The Wave of the Future

About the Project

The Chapter Project gives students an opportunity to explore periodic functions by examining tides. Students consider how the periodic nature of tides creates special problems in the design of power plants. They determine amplitude and period of a function that models tidal cycles and graph a periodic function. They discuss whether tidal power plants are practical sources of electricity.

Introducing the Project

• Ask students if they have observed high tide and low tide.

• Explain that the range of tidal height (the difference between low tide and high tide) varies throughout the month.

• Ask students what they think a graph of tidal height might look like.

Activity 1: Estimating

Students estimate the period and amplitude of a function that models tidal cycles.

Activity 2: Modeling

Students graphically show the relationship between phases of the moon and tidal ranges. They also research the relationship between the phases of the moon and the forces controlling the tides.

Activity 3: Researching

Students research advantages, disadvantages, and the practicality of tidal power.

Finishing the Project

You may wish to plan a project day on which students share their completed projects. Encourage students to explain their processes as well as their results.

• Ask students to share their conclusions about tidal power plants and conclude whether they are practical sources of electricity for the future.

• Ask students to share their insights that resulted from completing the project, such as any shortcuts they found for determining the period of a function or for sketching periodic functions.

Take it to the NET

Visit PHSchool.com for information, student links, and teacher support for this project.

• •

Algebra 2 Chapter 13   Project   **29**

✔ Checkpoint Quiz 1
· ·
Use with Lessons 13-1 through 13-3.

Find the period and amplitude of each periodic function.

1.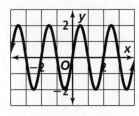

2.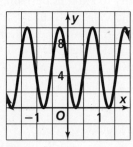

3.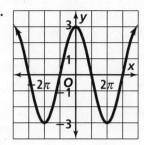

The measure θ of an angle in standard position is given. Find the exact values of cos θ and sin θ for each angle measure.

4. $-120°$ **5.** $135°$ **6.** $\frac{\pi}{3}$ radians

Convert each angle measure into its equivalent in radians or degrees.

7. $315°$ **8.** $\frac{5\pi}{6}$ radians   **9.** $\frac{3\pi}{4}$ radians

10. Open-Ended Sketch a periodic function with period 2.5 and amplitude 5.

- - - - ✂ -

✔ Checkpoint Quiz 2
· ·
Use with Lessons 13-4 through 13-7.

Graph each function in the interval from -2π to 2π.

1. $y = -2 \cos \frac{1}{2}x$ **2.** $y = \sin(x - \pi)$ **3.** $y = \tan \frac{1}{4}x$

4. $y = -\sin x + 1$ **5.** $y = -\tan \frac{1}{2}x$ **6.** $y = 3 \cos\left(x - \frac{\pi}{2}\right)$

7. $y = \tan \frac{\pi}{2}x$ **8.** $y = -\cos \frac{\pi}{2}x$ **9.** $y = 2 \sin 2x$

10. Sketch the graph of $y = \cos 2x$ after a translation of $\frac{\pi}{2}$ units to the left and 1 unit up.

Chapter Test

Form A

Chapter 13

Determine whether each function *is* or *is not* periodic. If it is periodic, find the period and amplitude.

1.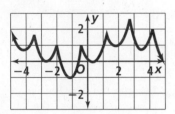

2.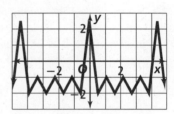

Find the measure of an angle between 0° and 360° coterminal with each given angle.

3. $-323°$

4. $-4°$

5. $370°$

Write each measure in radians. Express the answer in terms of π and also as a decimal rounded to the nearest hundredth.

6. $315°$

7. $-450°$

8. $210°$

Write each measure in degrees.

9. $\frac{7\pi}{4}$

10. $\frac{5\pi}{3}$

11. 6π

How many cycles does each sine function have in the interval from 0 to 2π? Find the amplitude and period of each function.

12.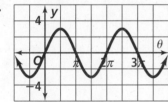

13.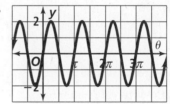

14. Open-Ended Sketch the graph of a periodic function.

15. A gear with a radius of 4 in. turns through an angle of $\frac{7\pi}{8}$ radians. What distance does a point on the edge of the gear travel as the gear turns through this angle? Round your answer to the nearest tenth.

Chapter Test (continued)   Form A

Chapter 13

Find the amplitude and period of each function. Then sketch one cycle of the graph of each function.

16. $y = 3 \sin 4x$ **17.** $y = -2 \sin 8x$

Solve each equation in the interval from 0 to 2π. Round to the nearest hundredth.

18. $\cos \pi t = -1$ **19.** $4 \cos t = -2\sqrt{3}$

20. $\cos\left(\frac{\pi}{2}t\right) = \frac{1}{2}$ **21.** $3 \cos \pi t = -2$

Write a cosine function for each description. Assume that $a > 0$.

22. amplitude $= \frac{1}{4}$, period $= 2$ **23.** amplitude $= 3$, period $= \frac{\pi}{2}$

Graph each function in the interval from 0 to 2π.

24. $y = 2 \sin 2\theta$ **25.** $y = \cos 2\theta$ **26.** $y = \frac{1}{2} \tan \frac{\pi}{2}\theta$

Write an equation for each translation.

27. $y = \cos x$, 4 units to the left

28. $y = \sin x$, $\frac{\pi}{4}$ units right, 2 units up

Evaluate each expression. Write your answer in exact form. If the expression is undefined, write *undefined*.

29. $\sec(-30°)$ **30.** $\csc 270°$

31. $\cot 210°$ **32.** $\sec 90°$

Graph each function in the interval from 0 to 2π.

33. $y = \csc \theta - 1$ **34.** $y = \sec 2\theta$

35. Writing Describe the affect of a vertical shift on the amplitude of a periodic function.

Chapter Test

Form B

Chapter 13

Determine whether each function *is* or *is not* periodic. If it is periodic, find the period and amplitude.

1.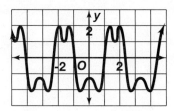

2.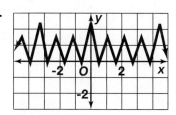

Find the measure of an angle between 0° and 360° coterminal with each given angle.

3. $-399°$

4. $-16°$

5. $390°$

Write each measure in radians. Express the answer in terms of π and also as a decimal rounded to the nearest hundredth.

6. $540°$

7. $-330°$

8. $450°$

Write each measure in degrees.

9. 5π

10. $\dfrac{7\pi}{6}$

11. $\dfrac{4\pi}{3}$

How many cycles does each sine function have in the interval from 0 to 2π? Find the amplitude and period of each function.

12.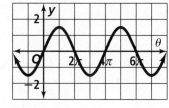

13.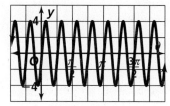

14. **Open-Ended** Sketch a circle with a central angle whose intercepted arc measures $\frac{2}{9}$ unit. Label the length of the radius and measure of the central angle (in radians).

15. A gear with a radius of 19 cm turns through an angle of $\frac{2\pi}{3}$ radians. What distance does a point on the edge of the gear travel as the gear turns through this angle? Round your answer to the nearest tenth.

Chapter Test (continued)   Form B

Chapter 13

Find the amplitude and period of each function. Then sketch one cycle of the graph of each function.

16. $y = -\sin 4x$

17. $y = 5 \sin 8x$

Solve each equation in the interval from 0 to 2π. Round to the nearest hundredth.

18. $-4 \cos t = 2$

19. $\cos 3t = -1$

20. $\cos\left(\dfrac{\pi}{4}t\right) = \dfrac{\sqrt{3}}{2}$

21. $-2 \cos\left(\dfrac{\pi}{2}t\right) = \dfrac{1}{2}$

Write a sine function for each description. Assume that $a > 0$.

22. amplitude $= \dfrac{1}{2}$, period $= 3$

23. amplitude $= 2$, period $= \dfrac{\pi}{4}$

Graph each function in the interval from 0 to 2π.

24. $y = 3 \sin 2\theta$

25. $y = 2 \cos 2\theta$

26. $y = \dfrac{1}{3} \tan \theta$

Write an equation for each translation.

27. $y = \sin x$, 4 units right

28. $y = \cos x$, 1 unit left, 3 units up

Evaluate each expression. Write your answer in exact form. If the expression is undefined, write *undefined*.

29. $\csc(-45°)$

30. $\sec 135°$

31. $\cot 210°$

32. $\csc 180°$

Graph each function in the interval from 0 to 2π.

33. $y = \sec\left(\theta + \dfrac{\pi}{2}\right)$

34. $y = \csc 2\theta$

35. Writing Describe the affect of a phase shift on the period of a periodic function.

Alternative Assessment
Form C
Chapter 13

• •

Give complete answers and show all your work.

TASK 1

   a. Suppose you are at the center of a circle with a radius of 1 mi. How far left or right and how far up or down must you move in order to end up on the boundary of the circle, with a final angle of 22° with respect to the horizontal axis?

   b. Convert 22° to radians and redo part a. How do your answers change?

   c. If you started 1 mi to the right of your original position, how far would you have to travel along the boundary of the circle to reach the same final point as in part a? Did you choose to work in radians or in degrees? Why? Explain your answer.

   d. Give an example of a real-world situation that could be modeled by part a or part c.

TASK 2

   a. In general, does Earth have a constant period in its orbit around the sun? If so, what is the period? If not, explain why not.

   b. Explain whether Earth's orbit around the sun is best modeled by a quadratic, a periodic, or a rational function.

   c. In general terms, what is the amplitude of Earth's orbit around the sun?

   d. Let $f(t)$ be a sine or cosine function representing the distance of Earth from the sun in its orbit around the sun, where t represents time in 365-day years. How does the amplitude, phase shift, and vertical shift of $f(t)$ affect the amount of time that elapses between the maximum and minimum distances the Earth is from the sun?

   e. Use the information and result from part d to write a sine function $f(t)$ that can be used to determine the amount of time that elapses between the maximum and minimum distances the Earth is from the sun.

   f. Use your graphing calculator to graph the sine function in part d. Use the graph to determine the amount of time that elapses between the maximum and minimum distances the Earth is from the sun.

TASK 3

   a. Write a sine function with amplitude 2 and period 4.

   b. Write a cosine function with amplitude 3 and period $\frac{\pi}{2}$, which has been shifted up 1 unit.

   c. Write a tangent function with period 3π.

   d. Can the graph of a tangent function be shifted 3 units to the left? Explain your answer.

   e. Can the graph of a secant function be shifted 2 units right and 5 units up? Explain your answer.

TASK 4

   a. Explain how you can determine the locations of the asymptotes for the graph of a tangent function. Give an example.

   b. Explain how the graphs of $y = \sin 2\theta$ and $y = \csc 2\theta$ are related.

   c. Explain how the graphs of $y = -3 \cos \theta$ and $y = -3 \sec \theta$ are related.

Cumulative Review

· ·

Chapters 1–13

For Exercises 1–12, choose the correct letter.

1. Which of these is the solution of $\begin{cases} y > x - 2 \\ y < 3 \end{cases}$?

   A. 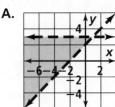   **B.** 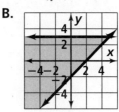   **C.** 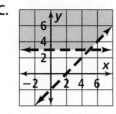   **D.**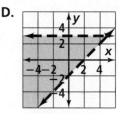

2. When $f(x) = 3x^2$ and $g(x) = x - 5$, what is the value of $f(g(3))$?

   A. 13   **B.** 22   **C.** 12   **D.** 36

3. Find $\begin{bmatrix} 6 & 2 \\ 0 & -1 \end{bmatrix} + \begin{bmatrix} 3 & 1 \\ -1 & 0 \end{bmatrix}$

   A. $\begin{bmatrix} 9 & 3 \\ -1 & -1 \end{bmatrix}$ **B.** $\begin{bmatrix} 9 & 3 \\ 0 & 0 \end{bmatrix}$ **C.** $\begin{bmatrix} 3 & 1 \\ 1 & -1 \end{bmatrix}$ **D.** $\begin{bmatrix} 9 & 3 \\ 0 & -2 \end{bmatrix}$

4. Solve the system $\begin{cases} x + y + z = 4 \\ x + 2y - z = 2. \\ 3z = x - 3y \end{cases}$

   A. $x = 3, y = 0, z = 1$ **B.** $x = 0, y = 3, z = 1$

   C. $x = 3, y = 1, z = 0$ **D.** no solution

5. Which polynomial function has zeros at 1, 2, and 4?

   A. $f(x) = (x + 1)(x + 2)(x + 4)$ **B.** $f(x) = x^2 - 3x + 2$

   C. $f(x) = x^3 - 7x^2 + 14x - 8$ **D.** $f(x) = x^3 - 7x^2 - 10x + 8$

6. Simplify $\dfrac{x - 5}{25 - x^2}$.

   A. $\dfrac{1}{x + 5}$ **B.** $x + 5$ **C.** $5 - x$ **D.** $\dfrac{-1}{5 + x}$

7. Which of these is the graph of $y = e^x$?

   A. 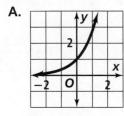   **B.** 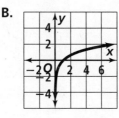   **C.** 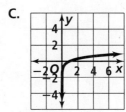   **D.**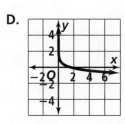

· ·

Cumulative Review (continued)

Chapters 1–13

8. Which of the following is the equation of an inverse variation passing through $\left(2, \frac{1}{3}\right)$?

   A. $y = \frac{3}{2x}$ **B.** $y = \frac{2}{3x}$ **C.** $y = \frac{2}{3}x$ **D.** $xy = \frac{3}{2}$

9. Which of the following is equivalent to $\frac{3\pi}{4}$ radians?

   A. $0.75°$ **B.** $135°$ **C.** $270°$ **D.** $175°$

10. Divide $x^2 - 2x - 35$ by $(x + 5)$.

    A. $x - 7$ **B.** $x + 7$ **C.** $-(x - 7)$ **D.** $-(x + 7)$

11. Simplify $e^{\ln x} + \ln e - \ln e^x - \ln 1$.

    A. $e^{\ln x} - \ln e^2$ **B.** $\ln (e^2 x - 1)$ **C.** 0 **D.** 1

12. What is the axis of symmetry of the graph $y = 2(x - 3)^2 + 4$?

    A. $x = 3$ **B.** $x = 2$ **C.** $y = 3$ **D.** $y = 4$

Compare the quantity in Column A with that in Column B. Choose the best answer.

    A. The quantity in Column A is greater.

    B. The quantity in Column B is greater.

    C. The two quantities are equal.

    D. The relationship cannot be determined on the basis of the information supplied.

Column A	Column B
13. i	$\sqrt{-1}$
14. $\sin 30°$	$\cos 30°$

Find each answer.

15. Write the equation of the line with $m = 3$ passing through $(12, 1)$.

16. What is the slope of the line $x = 2$?

17. What is the length of the arc intercepted by a central angle measuring $40°$ of a circle of radius 2 cm?

18. If $\cos x = \frac{\sqrt{3}}{2}$, what is $\sec x$?

19. **Open-Ended** Write a 3×2 matrix.

20. **Writing** Explain how you can obtain the graph of $y = \cos \left(x - \frac{\pi}{2}\right) + 1$ from the graph of $y = \cos x$.

Chapter 13 Answers

Practice 13-1

1. not periodic **2.** periodic; 2 **3.** periodic; $3\frac{1}{4}$ **4.** any two points on the graph whose distance between them is one period; sample: $(0,2)$ and $(3\frac{1}{3}, 2)$; $3\frac{1}{3}$ **5.** any two points on the graph whose distance between them is one period; sample: $(0,0)$ and $(4\frac{1}{4}, 0)$; $4\frac{1}{4}$ **6.** any two points on the graph whose distance between them is one period; sample: $(0,2)$ and $(4,2)$; 4 **7.** $2\frac{1}{8}$; 1

8. 3; 2 **9.** 2; 3 **10.** 6; $2\frac{1}{8}$ **11.** 6; $1\frac{3}{4}$ **12.** $1\frac{2}{3}$; $1\frac{3}{4}$ **13.** 4; 2

14. 5; $1\frac{5}{8}$ **15.** $1\frac{2}{3}$; 2 **16.** 4; $2\frac{1}{2}$ **17.** 5; $1\frac{1}{2}$ **18.** $2\frac{1}{2}$, $1\frac{5}{8}$

Practice 13-2

1.
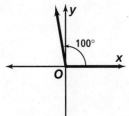

2.
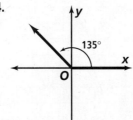

3.
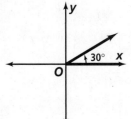

4.
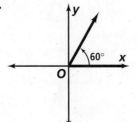

5.
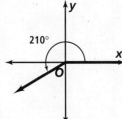

6.
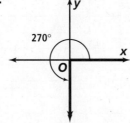

7.
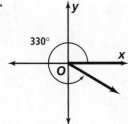

8.
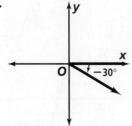

9.
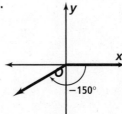

10.
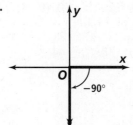

11.
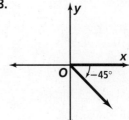

12.
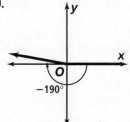

13.
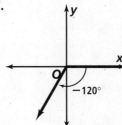

14.
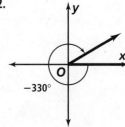

15.
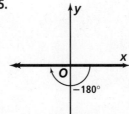

16.
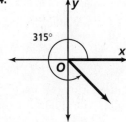

17.
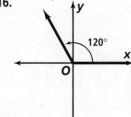

18.
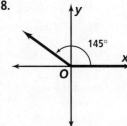

19.
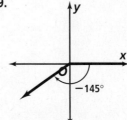

20.
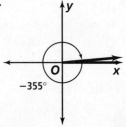

Chapter 13 Answers (continued)

21. $260°$ **22.** $300°$ **23.** $135°$ **24.** $215°$ **25.** $12°$ **26.** $345°$
27. $122°$ **28.** $124°$ **29.** $340°$ **30.** $61°$ **31.** $49°$ **32.** $322°$
33. $16°$ **34.** $150°$ **35.** $27°$ **36.** $30°$ **37.** $300°$ **38.** $80°$
39. $190°$ **40.** $10°$ **41.** $20°$ **42.** $98°$ **43.** $120°$ **44.** $46°$
45. $240°$ **46.** $100°$ **47.** $138°$ **48.** $30°$ **49.** $233°$ **50.** $17°$

51. $\left(\frac{\sqrt{2}}{2}, \frac{\sqrt{2}}{2}\right); (0.71, 0.71)$

52. $\left(-\frac{\sqrt{2}}{2}, -\frac{\sqrt{2}}{2}\right); (-0.71, -0.71)$

53. $\left(-\frac{\sqrt{2}}{2}, \frac{\sqrt{2}}{2}\right); (-0.71, 0.71)$

54. $\left(\frac{\sqrt{2}}{2}, -\frac{\sqrt{2}}{2}\right); (0.71, -0.71)$

55. $\left(\frac{\sqrt{3}}{2}, -\frac{1}{2}\right); (0.87, -0.5)$ **56.** $\left(\frac{\sqrt{3}}{2}, \frac{1}{2}\right); (0.87, 0.5)$

57. $\left(-\frac{\sqrt{3}}{2}, \frac{1}{2}\right); (-0.87, 0.5)$

58. $\left(-\frac{\sqrt{3}}{2}, -\frac{1}{2}\right); (-0.87, -0.5)$

59. $\left(\frac{1}{2}, -\frac{\sqrt{3}}{2}\right); (0.5, -0.87)$ **60.** $\left(\frac{1}{2}, \frac{\sqrt{3}}{2}\right); (0.5, 0.87)$

61. $\left(-\frac{1}{2}, -\frac{\sqrt{3}}{2}\right); (-0.5, -0.87)$ **62.** $\left(-\frac{1}{2}, \frac{\sqrt{3}}{2}\right); (-0.5, 0.87)$

63. $(0, -1); (0, -1)$ **64.** $(1, 0); (1, 0)$ **65.** $(1, 0); (1, 0)$

66. $(0, 1); (0, 1)$ **67.** $\left(-\frac{\sqrt{2}}{2}, \frac{\sqrt{2}}{2}\right); (-0.71, 0.71)$

68. $\left(-\frac{1}{2}, \frac{\sqrt{3}}{2}\right); (-0.5, 0.87)$ **69.** $-60°$ **70.** $120°$ **71.** $315°$

Practice 13-3

1. $\frac{\pi}{4}$ **2.** $\frac{\pi}{2}$ **3.** $\frac{\pi}{6}$ **4.** $\frac{5\pi}{6}$ **5.** π **6.** $\frac{4\pi}{3}$ **7.** $\frac{3\pi}{2}$

8. $\frac{5\pi}{3}$ **9.** 2π **10.** $\frac{2\pi}{9}$ **11.** $\frac{4\pi}{9}$ **12.** $\frac{11\pi}{18}$ **13.** $\frac{8\pi}{9}$ **14.** $\frac{10\pi}{9}$

15. $\frac{11\pi}{9}$ **16.** $180°$ **17.** $360°$ **18.** $150°$ **19.** $135°$ **20.** $270°$

21. $30°$ **22.** $210°$ **23.** $330°$ **24.** $60°$ **25.** $240°$ **26.** $225°$

27. $315°$ **28.** $120°$ **29.** $20°$ **30.** $40°$ **31.** $\frac{\sqrt{3}}{2}; \frac{1}{2}$

32. $\frac{1}{2}; \frac{\sqrt{3}}{2}$ **33.** $-\frac{\sqrt{2}}{2}; -\frac{\sqrt{2}}{2}$ **34.** $\frac{\sqrt{2}}{2}; -\frac{\sqrt{2}}{2}$

35. $-\frac{\sqrt{3}}{2}; \frac{1}{2}$ **36.** $-\frac{1}{2}; -\frac{\sqrt{3}}{2}$ **37.** $\frac{\sqrt{3}}{2}; -\frac{1}{2}$

38. $-\frac{1}{2}; \frac{\sqrt{3}}{2}$

39. 11.0 in. **40.** 39.8 cm **41.** 10.5 cm **42.** 92.2 cm **43.** 2.1 ft
44. 15.7 m **45.** about 17.8 in. **46.** 1.2 m

Practice 13-4

1. $4; 2\pi; y = 4 \sin \theta$ **2.** $1.5; \frac{\pi}{2}; y = 1.5 \sin 4\theta$

3. $2; 3\pi; y = -2 \sin \frac{2}{3}\theta$ **4.** $1; 6\pi; y = \sin \frac{1}{3}\theta$

5. $2.5; \pi; y = -2.5 \sin 2\theta$ **6.** $4; \pi; y = -4 \sin 2\theta$

7. 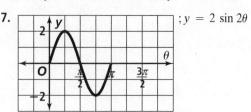 $; y = 2 \sin 2\theta$

8. 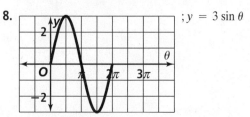 $; y = 3 \sin \theta$

9. 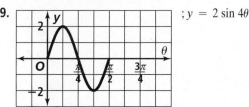 $; y = 2 \sin 4\theta$

10. 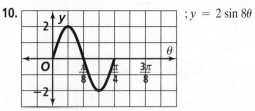 $; y = 2 \sin 8\theta$

11. 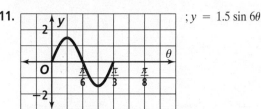 $; y = 1.5 \sin 6\theta$

12. 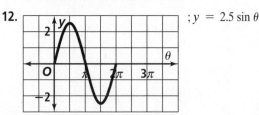 $; y = 2.5 \sin \theta$

13.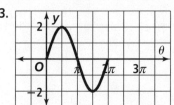

14.

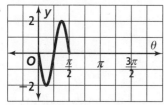

15.

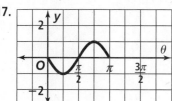

16.

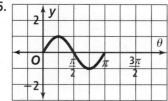

17.

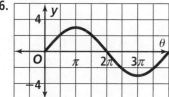

18.

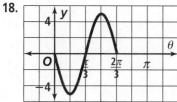

19.

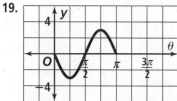

20.

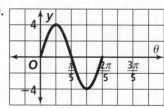

21.

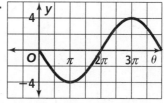

22. about −0.1 **23.** about 0.2 **24.** about 0.2 **25.** 0.3
26. about 0.1 **27.** about 0.2 **28.** −0.3 **29.** about −0.2

Practice 13-5

1.

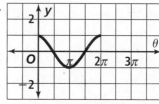

2.

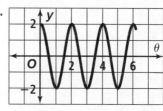

3.

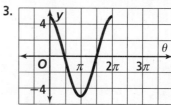

4.

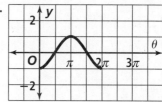

5.

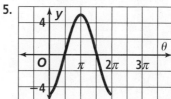

6.

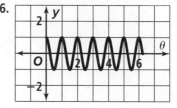

7.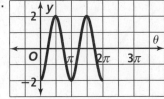

8.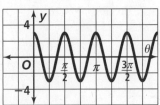

9.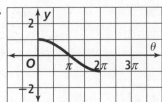

10.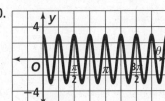

11.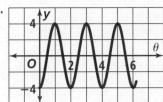

12.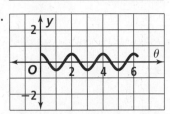

13.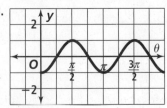

14.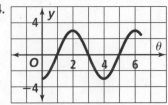

15.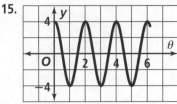

16. $y = 6 \cos \frac{2\pi}{5} t$ **17.** $y = -5 \cos \theta$

18. $y = 4 \cos 2\theta$ **19.** $y = 3 \cos 4\theta$ **20.** $2\pi; 1; \pi; 0, 2\pi; \frac{\pi}{2}, \frac{3\pi}{2}$

21. $\pi; 4; 0, \pi, 2\pi; \frac{\pi}{2}, \frac{3\pi}{2}; \frac{\pi}{4}, \frac{3\pi}{4}, \frac{5\pi}{4}, \frac{7\pi}{4}$

22. $2\pi; 5; \pi; 0, 2\pi; \frac{\pi}{2}, \frac{3\pi}{2}$ **23.** $0.24, 1.85, 2.34, 3.95, 4.43, 6.04$

24. 2.36 **25.** $1.00, 3.00, 5.00$ **26.** 1.34 **27.** $0.84, 5.44$ **28.** 0

29. $2.67, 5.33$ **30.** 4.19 **31.** 3.14 **32.** $y = 2\pi \cos 2\pi\theta$

33. $y = \frac{1}{2} \cos 2\theta$

Practice 13-6

1. $\pi; \frac{\pi}{2}, \frac{3\pi}{2}$ **2.** $2\pi; \pi$ **3.** $4\pi; 2\pi$ **4.** $\frac{\pi}{2}; \frac{\pi}{4}, \frac{3\pi}{4}, \frac{5\pi}{4}, \frac{7\pi}{4}$

5. $2; 1, 3, 5$ **6.** $1; \frac{1}{2}, \frac{3}{2}, \frac{5}{2}, \frac{7}{2}, \frac{9}{2}, \frac{11}{2}$ **7.** $\frac{\pi}{2}; \frac{\pi}{4}, \frac{3\pi}{4}, \frac{5\pi}{4}, \frac{7\pi}{4}$

8. $\pi; \frac{\pi}{2}, \frac{3\pi}{2}$ **9.** $1; \frac{1}{2}, \frac{3}{2}, \frac{5}{2}, \frac{7}{2}, \frac{9}{2}, \frac{11}{2}$

10.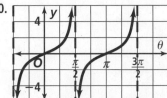

11.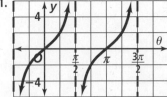

12.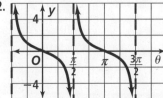

13.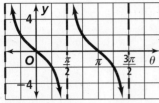

14.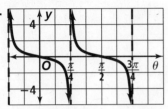

15.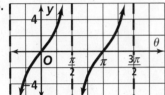

16.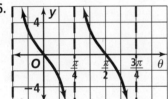

17.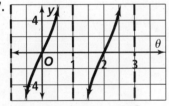

18.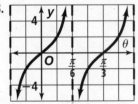

19.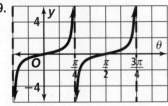

20.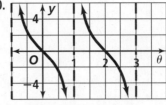

21.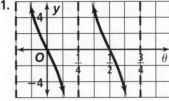

22.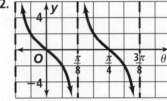

23.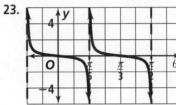

24.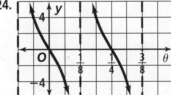

25.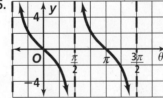

26.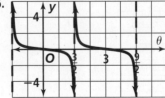

27.

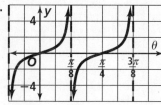

28. $\frac{\pi}{4}$ **29.** π **30.** 2π **31.** undefined **32.** 1 **33.** -1

34. undefined

35.

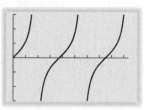 ; 200, undefined, -200

Xmin=0   Ymin=−300
Xmax=470 Ymax=300
Xscl=50   Yscl=100

36.

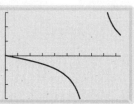 ; $-14.9, -31.1, -50.1$

Xmin=0   Ymin=−300
Xmax=470 Ymax=300
Xscl=50   Yscl=100

37.

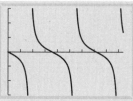 ; -50, undefined, 50

Xmin=0   Ymin=−300
Xmax=470 Ymax=300
Xscl=50   Yscl=100

Practice 13-7

1.

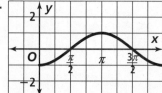

2.

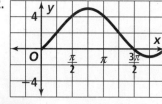

3.

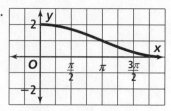

4.

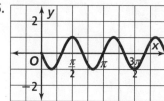

5.

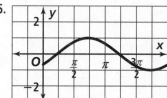

6.

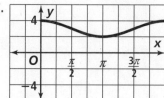

7.

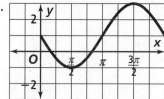

8.

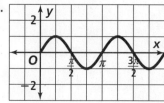

9.

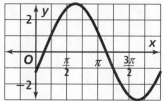

10.

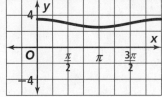

11.

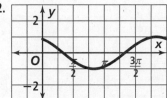

12.

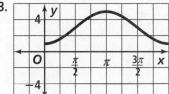

13.

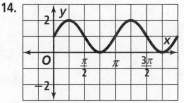

14.

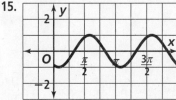

15.

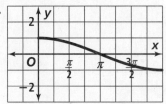

26.

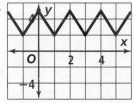

27.

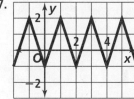

28.

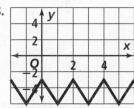

29.

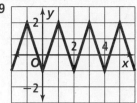

30.

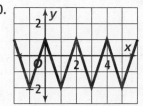

31.

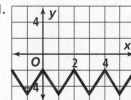

16. $y = \sin x - 2$ **17.** $y = \cos (x + \pi)$ **18.** $y = \cos x + \frac{\pi}{4}$

19. $y = \sin (x - 3.2)$ **20.** 3; 2π; none; 2 units up

21. 2; 2π; $\frac{\pi}{2}$ units left; none **22.** 1; π; none; 1 unit up

23. 1; 2π; $\frac{\pi}{3}$ units right; none **24.** $\frac{1}{2}$; 2π; none; 3 units down

25. 1; 4π; none; 2 units down

32. -2; 2 units to the left **33.** 1; 1 unit to the right

34. -1.5; 1.5 units to the left **35.** 1; 1 unit to the right

36. $\frac{\pi}{2}$, $\frac{\pi}{2}$ units to the right **37.** $-\pi$; π units to the left

Practice 13-8

1. 0.86 **2.** 2 **3.** -1.10 **4.** -1 **5.** undefined **6.** -1.07

7. 0.58 **8.** 14.14 **9.** -1.00 **10.** undefined **11.** -1.01

12. 1.41 **13.** $\sqrt{2}$; 1.41 **14.** undefined **15.** $\frac{2\sqrt{3}}{3}$; 1.15

16. 2 **17.** undefined **18.** $-\sqrt{2}$; -1.41 **19.** undefined **20.** 1

21. undefined **22.** $\frac{2\sqrt{3}}{3}$; 1.15 **23.** $-\frac{2\sqrt{3}}{3}$; -1.15 **24.** 2

25. $\frac{3}{2}$ **26.** $\frac{5}{2}$ **27.** $\frac{10}{7}$ **28.** $-\frac{3}{2}$

29.

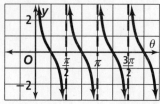

30.

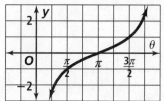

31.

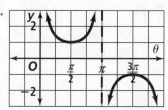

32.

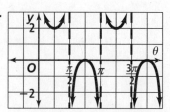

33.

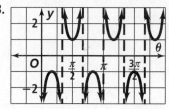

34.

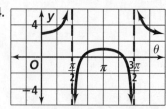

35.

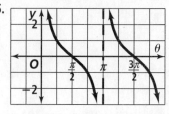

36.

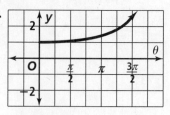

37.

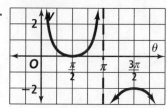

38. 1.73 **39.** undefined **40.** 0.36 **41.** −5.76
42. 1.56 **43.** 1.02 **44.** 2.75 **45.** −2
46a.

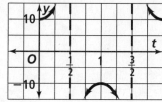

46b. about 14.14 ft **46c.** 10 ft

Reteaching 13-1
1. 6; 2 **2.** not periodic **3.** 3; 2

Reteaching 13-2
1. $\left(-\frac{\sqrt{3}}{2}, -\frac{1}{2}\right)$ **2.** $\left(\frac{\sqrt{3}}{2}, \frac{1}{2}\right)$ **3.** $\left(\frac{\sqrt{3}}{2}, \frac{1}{2}\right)$
4. $\left(\frac{\sqrt{2}}{2}, -\frac{\sqrt{2}}{2}\right)$ **5.** $\left(-\frac{1}{2}, \frac{\sqrt{3}}{2}\right)$ **6.** $\left(-\frac{\sqrt{2}}{2}, -\frac{\sqrt{2}}{2}\right)$

Reteaching 13-3
1. $\frac{\pi}{9} \approx 0.35$ **2.** $\frac{5\pi}{6} \approx 2.62$ **3.** $\frac{\pi}{4} \approx 0.79$

4. $-\frac{11\pi}{18} \approx -1.92$ **5.** $\frac{7\pi}{4} \approx 5.50$ **6.** $\frac{16\pi}{9} \approx 5.59$

7. −270° **8.** 300° **9.** 15° **10.** 288° **11.** −210° **12.** 810°

Reteaching 13-4
1.

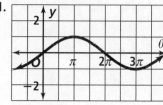

2. 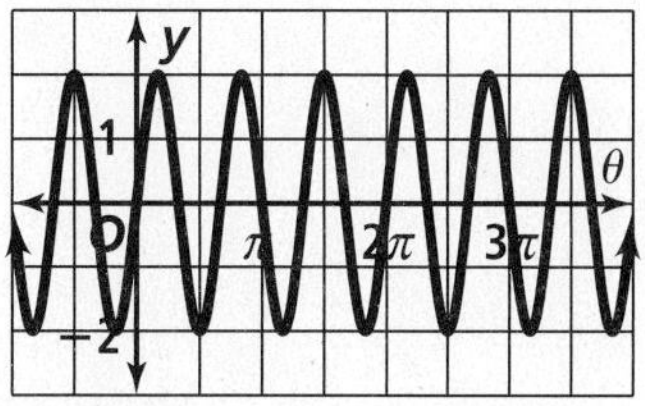

3. 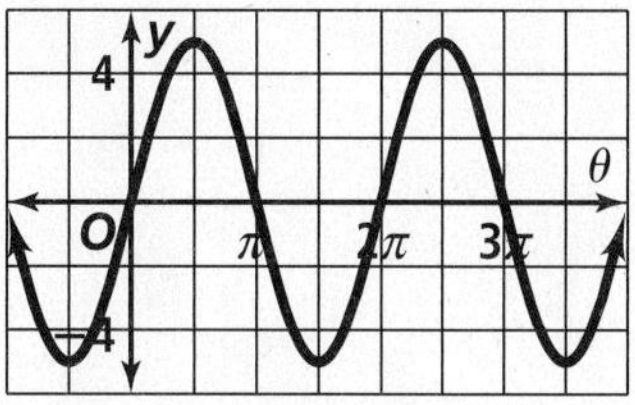

4. 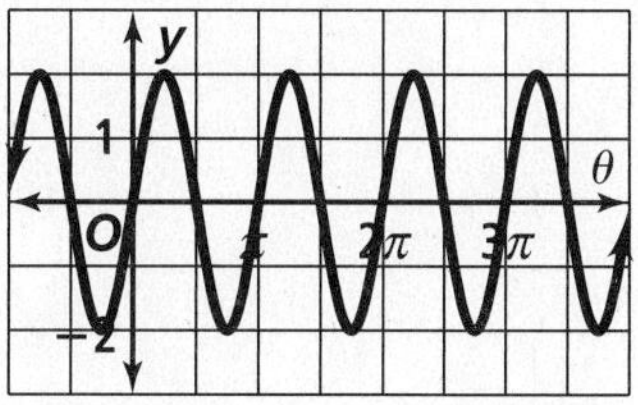

5. 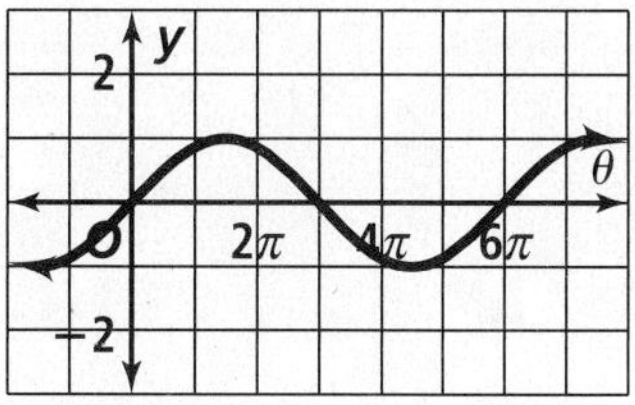

6. 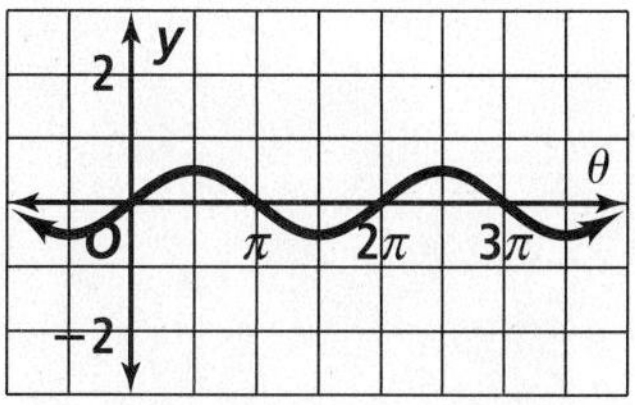

7. 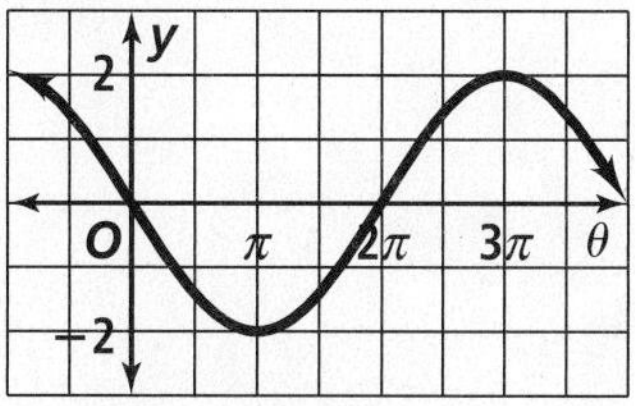

8. 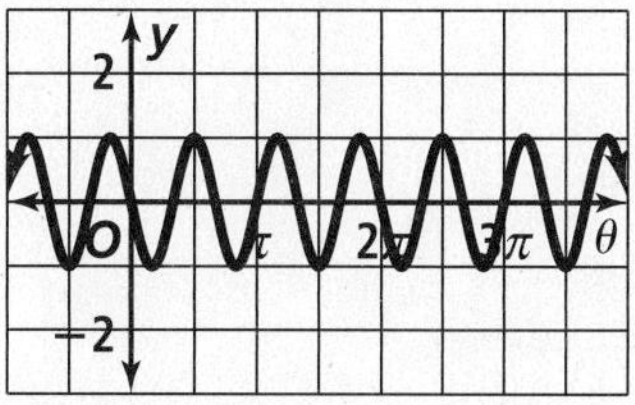

9. 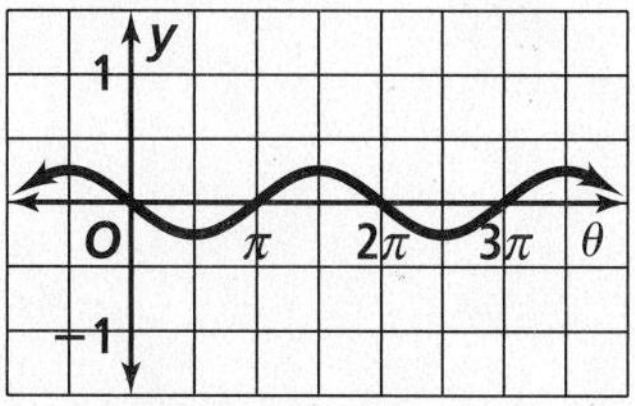

Reteaching 13-5

1. $\frac{1}{2}$; π; 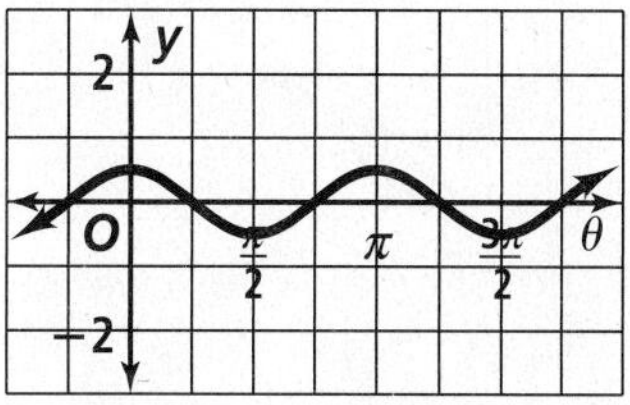

2. 3; 4π; 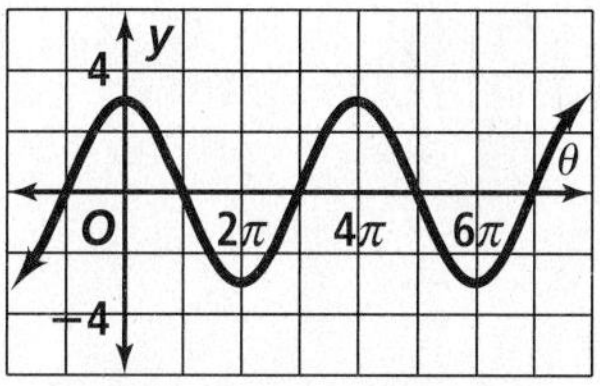

3. 1; $\frac{2}{3}\pi$; 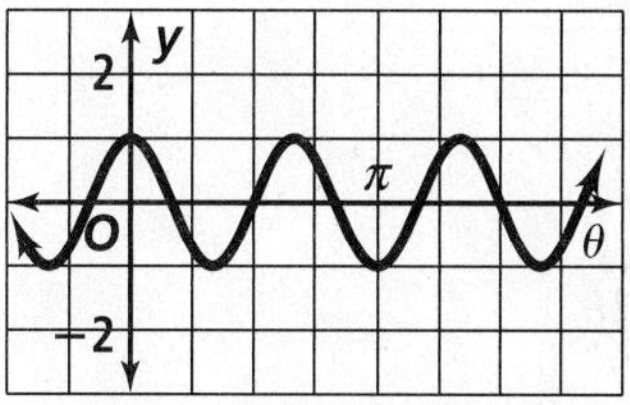

4. $\frac{1}{4}$; 2; 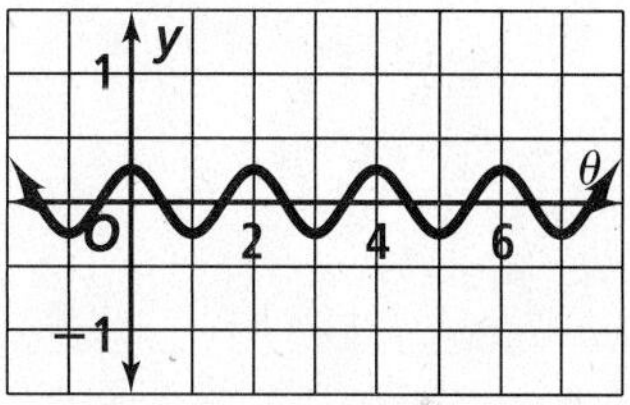

5. 2; 4π; 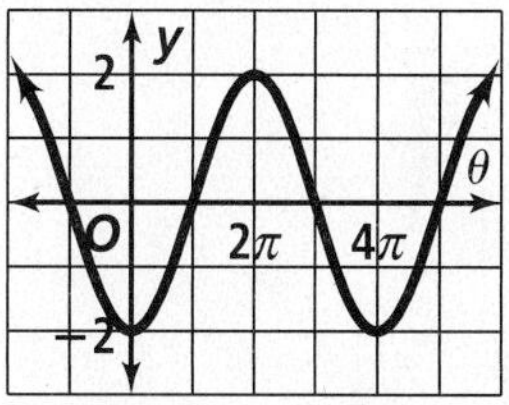

6. 2; $\frac{1}{3}$; 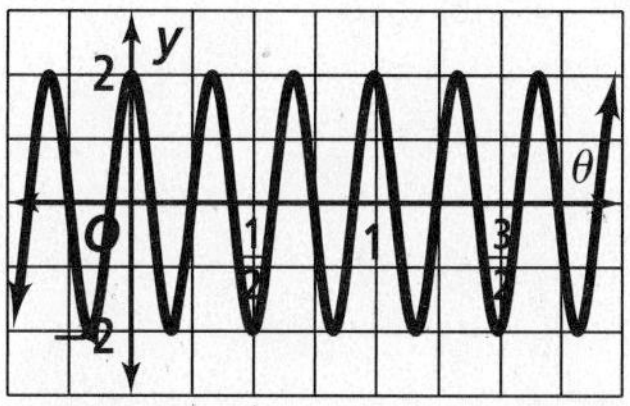

7. 2; 2π; 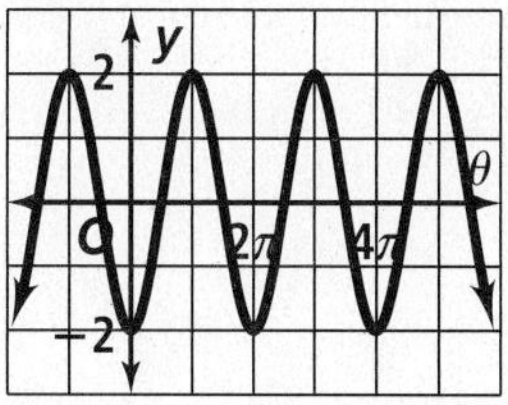

8. 1; 10π;

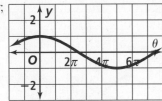

9. 2; π;

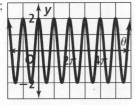

Reteaching 13-6

1. $\frac{\pi}{2}, \frac{\pi}{4}, \frac{3\pi}{4}, \frac{5\pi}{4}, \frac{7\pi}{4}$;

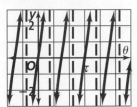

2. 2π; π;

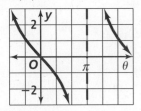

3. π; $\frac{\pi}{2}, \frac{3\pi}{2}$;

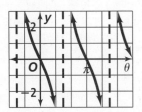

4. $\frac{\pi}{2}, \frac{\pi}{4}, \frac{3\pi}{4}, \frac{5\pi}{4}, \frac{7\pi}{4}$;

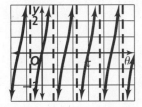

5. 2; 1, 3, 5;

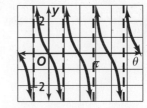

6. π; $\frac{\pi}{2}, \frac{3\pi}{2}$;

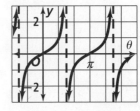

7. $\frac{\pi}{3}; \frac{\pi}{6}, \frac{\pi}{2}, \frac{5\pi}{6}, \frac{7\pi}{6}, \frac{3\pi}{2}, \frac{11\pi}{6}$;

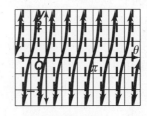

8. 2; 1, 3, 5;

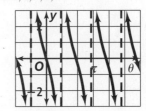

9. 4; 2, 6;

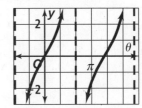

Reteaching 13-7

1.

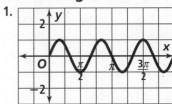

2.

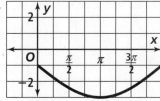

3.

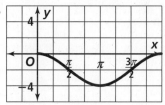

4.

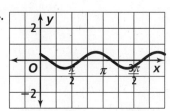

5.

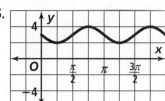

6.

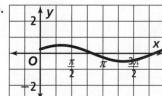

7.

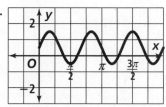

8.

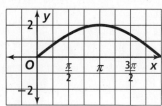

9.

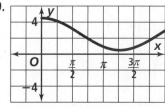

Reteaching 13-8

1.

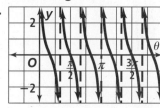

2.

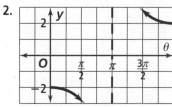

3.

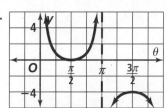

4.

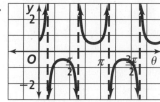

5.

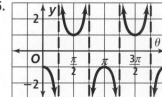

6.

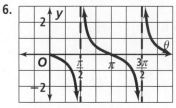

7.

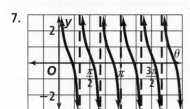

8.

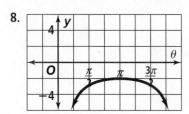

9.

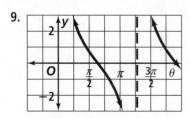

Enrichment 13-1

1. 2 **2.** 9 **3.** 8 **4.** 4 **5.** 7 **6.** 1 **7.** 5 **8.** 6 **9.** 3

A R I S T O T L E

Enrichment 13-2

1. about 1.16 miles **2.** 23.2 miles **3.** 13.92 miles
4. 0.1125 radians or about 6.4° **5.** 0.627 radians or about 35.9°

Enrichment 13-3

1. $\frac{S}{1} = \frac{S}{r}$ **2.** $A = s$ **3.** $A = \frac{S}{r}$ **4.** $S = rA$ **5.** π radians

6. $\frac{D}{360} = \frac{A}{2\pi}$ **7.** $S = \frac{\pi}{180} rD$ **8.** $S = 2\pi Vr$

9. $\frac{10\pi}{9}$ radians/s

Enrichment 13-4

1. 0.4226 **2.** 0.5878 **3.** 0.3256 **4.** 0.1908 **5.** 0.0872
6. 0.9703 **7.** 0.6561 **8.** 0.6157 **9.** 0.3746
DOG; LOG; LEG; BEG; BAG; RAG

Enrichment 13-5

1. 0.087156; 0.087156; 0.087156
2. $\frac{11\pi}{180}$; 0.190807; 0.190809; 0.190809; 0.190809
3. $\frac{13\pi}{90}$; 0.438212; 0.438372; 0.438371; 0.438371
4. $\frac{37\pi}{180}$; 0.600888; 0.601824; 0.601815; 0.601815

5. Answers may vary. Sample: The results indicate that $S_n(x)$ approximates sin x to a greater degree of accuracy as n increases. For x small, $S_3(x)$ is a good approximation to sin x; indicating that sin $x \approx x$ for x small.
6. 0.996192; 0.996195; 0.996195
7. $\frac{11\pi}{180}$; 0.981571; 0.981627; 0.981627; 0.981627
8. $\frac{13\pi}{90}$; 0.897039; 0.898806; 0.898794; 0.898794
9. $\frac{37\pi}{180}$; 0.791489; 0.798735; 0.798635; 0.798636

10. Answers may vary. Sample: The results indicate that $C_n(x)$ approximates cos x to a greater degree of accuracy as n increases. For x small, $C_2(x)$ is a good approximation to cos x; indicating that cos $x \approx 1$ for x small.

Enrichment 13-6

1. $(-a, b)$ **2.** $(-a, -b)$

3. $\frac{1}{2}$; $-\frac{1}{2}$; $\frac{\sqrt{2}}{2}$; $-\frac{\sqrt{2}}{2}$; $\frac{\sqrt{3}}{2}$; $-\frac{\sqrt{3}}{2}$; odd; $f(-x) = -f(x)$

4. $\frac{\sqrt{3}}{2}$; $\frac{\sqrt{3}}{2}$; $\frac{\sqrt{2}}{2}$; $\frac{\sqrt{2}}{2}$; $\frac{1}{2}$; $\frac{1}{2}$; even; $f(-x) = f(x)$

5. symmetrical about the origin; odd **6.** symmetrical about the y-axis; even **7.** symmetrical about the origin; odd

Enrichment 13-7

1. 14 **2.** 264 **3.** 139

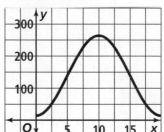

4. 125 **5.** 20; $\frac{\pi}{10}$ **6.** $y = 125 \cos \frac{\pi}{10} x$ **7.** 10; 139

8. $y = 125 \cos \frac{\pi}{10}(x - 10) + 139$

Enrichment 13-8

1. 1 **2.** sin $A = y$; cos $A = x$ **3.** $(\cos A, \sin A)$
4. $\sqrt{(\cos A - 0)^2 + (\sin A - 0)^2} = 1$
5. $(\cos A)^2 + (\sin A)^2 = 1$
6. $\cos A = \pm\sqrt{1 - \sin^2 A}$

7. $\tan A = \frac{\sin A}{\cos A}$ **8.** $\tan A = \pm\frac{\sin A}{\sqrt{1 - \sin^2 A}}$

9. $\cot A = \pm\frac{\sqrt{1 - \sin^2 A}}{\sin A}$

10. $\sin A = \pm\sqrt{1 - \cos^2 A}$

11. $\cos A = \pm\sqrt{1 - \frac{1}{\csc^2 A}}$

12. $\tan A = \pm\dfrac{\sqrt{1 - \cos^2 A}}{\cos A}$

Chapter Project

Activity 1: Estimating
Location 1: 12 h 25 min, 2.1 ft; Location 2: 12 h 25 min, 2.85 ft

Activity 2: Modeling

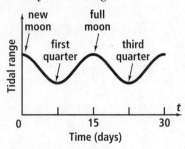

Check students' work.

Activity 3: Researching
Check students' work.

✔ Checkpoint Quiz 1

1. 2; 2 **2.** 1; 5 **3.** 4π; 3 **4.** $-\dfrac{1}{2}$; $-\dfrac{\sqrt{3}}{2}$ **5.** $-\dfrac{\sqrt{2}}{2}$; $\dfrac{\sqrt{2}}{2}$

6. $\dfrac{1}{2}$; $\dfrac{\sqrt{3}}{2}$ **7.** $\dfrac{7\pi}{4}$ **8.** 150° **9.** 135° **10.** Check students' work.

✔ Checkpoint Quiz 2

1.

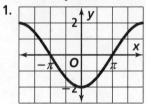

2.

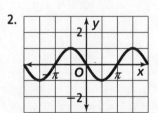

3.

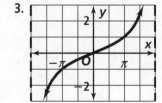

4.

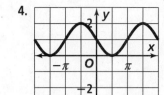

5.

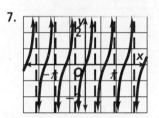

6.

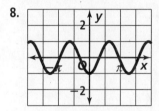

7.

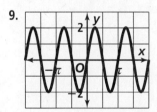

8.

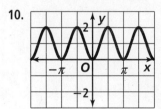

9.

10.

Chapter 13 Answers (continued)

Chapter Test, Form A

1. not periodic **2.** periodic; $4\frac{1}{4}$; $2\frac{3}{8}$ **3.** 37° **4.** 356° **5.** 10°

6. $\frac{7\pi}{4}$; 5.50 **7.** $-\frac{5\pi}{2}$; −7.85 **8.** $\frac{7\pi}{6}$; 3.67 **9.** 315°

10. 300° **11.** 1080° **12.** 1; 3; 2π **13.** 2; 2; π

14. Answers may vary. Sample:

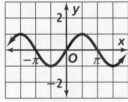

15. 11.0 in. **16.** 3; $\frac{\pi}{2}$;

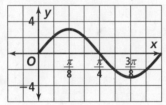

17. 2; $\frac{\pi}{4}$;

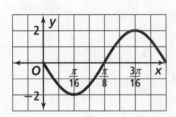

18. 1, 3, 5 **19.** 2.62, 3.67 **20.** 0.67, 3.33, 4.67

21. 0.73, 1.27, 2.73, 3.27, 4.73, 5.27 **22.** $y = \frac{1}{4}\cos \pi\, \theta$

23. $y = 3\cos 4\,\theta$

24.

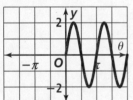

25.

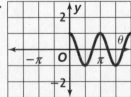

26.

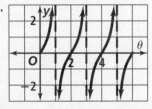

27. $y = \cos(x + 4)$ **28.** $y = \sin\left(x - \frac{\pi}{4}\right) + 2$

29. $\frac{2\sqrt{3}}{3}$ **30.** −1 **31.** $\sqrt{3}$ **32.** undefined

33.

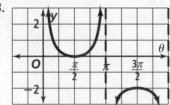

34.

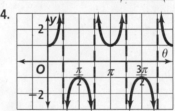

35. A vertical shift does not affect the amplitude of a periodic function.

Chapter Test, Form B

1. periodic; $3\frac{1}{4}$; $2\frac{1}{8}$ **2.** not periodic **3.** 321° **4.** 344° **5.** 30°

6. 3π; 9.42 **7.** $-\frac{11\pi}{6}$; −5.76 **8.** $\frac{5\pi}{2}$; 7.85 **9.** 900°

10. 210° **11.** 240° **12.** $\frac{1}{2}$; 1.5; 4π **13.** 8; 4; $\frac{\pi}{4}$

14. Answers may vary. Sample:

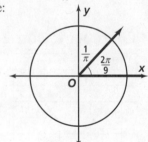

15. 39.8 cm **16.** 1; $\frac{\pi}{2}$;

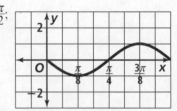

17. 5; $\frac{\pi}{4}$;

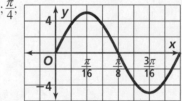

18. 2.09, 4.19 **19.** 1.05, 3.14, 5.24 **20.** 0.67

21. 1.16, 2.84, 5.16 **22.** $y = \frac{1}{2}\sin\frac{2\pi}{3}\,\theta$ **23.** $y = 2\sin 8\theta$

24.

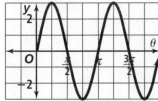

25.

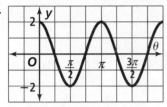

26.

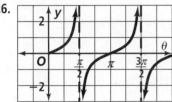

27. $y = \sin(x - 4)$ **28.** $y = \cos(x + 1) + 3$

29. $-\sqrt{2}$ **30.** $-\sqrt{2}$ **31.** $\sqrt{3}$ **32.** undefined

33.

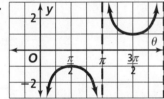

34.

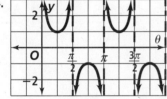

35. A phase shift does not affect the period of a periodic function.

Alternative Assessment, Form C

TASK 1 Scoring Guide:

a. ≈ 0.93 mi to the right, and ≈ 0.37 mi up

b. ≈ 0.38 radians; The answers stay the same.

c. ≈ 0.38 mi; It is easier to work in radians because, in radians, the arc length of a circle with a radius of 1 is given by the numerical value of the angle that created the arc.

d. Check students' work.

3 Student correctly finds the directions to move in part a. Student correctly converts degrees to radians, and finds that the results are the same as in part a. Student correctly determines arc length. Student provides a reasonable example that could be modeled by this situation.

2 Student correctly finds the directions to move in part a. Student converts degrees to radians and finds that the results are the same as in part a with only minor errors. Student correctly determines the arc length with only minor errors. Student provides an example that could be modeled by this situation.

1 Student finds the directions to move incorrectly in part a. Student incorrectly converts degrees to radians and does not compare the results with those in part a. Student incorrectly determines the arc length. Student does not provide an example that could be modeled by this situation.

0 Response is missing or inappropriate.

TASK 2 Scoring Guide:

a. Yes; in general, one 365-day year

b. Periodic, since every 365 days Earth is at the same basic position with respect to the sun.

c. The amplitude is one-half of the difference between the farthest Earth is from the sun and the closest Earth is from the sun during its orbit around the sun.

d. The amplitude, phase shift, and vertical shift of $f(t)$ does not affect the amount of time that elapses between the maximum and minimum distances the Earth is from the sun.

e. Answers may vary. Sample: $f(t) = \sin 2\pi t$.

f.   ; 0.5 yr

```
Xmin=0    Ymin=-3
Xmax=1    Ymax=3
Xscl=.25  Yscl=1
```

3 Student correctly identifies the period of Earth's orbit, and that Earth's orbit is best modeled by a periodic function. Student correctly describes the amplitude of Earth's orbit. Student correctly determines the amplitude, phase shift, and vertical shift of $f(t)$ does not affect time elapsed between max and min distance Earth is from the sun. Student determines a sine function $f(t)$ with no errors. Student uses a graphing calculator to correctly identify that one-half of a year elapses between max and min distances Earth is from the Sun.

2 Student correctly identifies the period of Earth's orbit, and that Earth's orbit is best modeled by a periodic function. Student describes the amplitude of Earth's orbit with only minor errors. Student correctly determines the amplitude, phase shift, and vertical shift of $f(t)$ does not affect time elapsed between max and min distance Earth is from Sun. Student determines a sine function $f(t)$ with only minor errors. Student correctly uses a graphing calculator, and identifies that one-half of a year elapses between max and min distances Earth is from the Sun with only minor errors.

1 Student identifies Earth's orbit as a periodic function. Student incorrectly describes the amplitude of Earth's orbit. Student incorrectly determines the affect of the amplitude, phase shift, and vertical shift of $f(t)$ on the time elapsed between max and min distances Earth is from the Sun. Student incorrectly determines a sine function $f(t)$. Student does not identify a time period of one-half of a year elapsing between max and min distances Earth is from the Sun.

0 Response is missing or inappropriate.

TASK 3 Scoring Guide:

a. Answers may vary. Sample: $y = 2 \sin \frac{\pi}{2} x$

b. Answers may vary. Sample: $y = 3 \cos 4x + 1$

c. Answers may vary. Sample: $y = \tan \frac{1}{3} x$

d. yes; Check students' work.

e. yes; Check students' work.

3 Student correctly writes three functions. Student gives an accurate explanation of shifting tangent and secant functions.

2 Student writes two of the three functions correctly. Student gives a reasonable explanation on shifting tangent and secant functions.

1 Student writes one of the three functions correctly, or has minor errors in all three functions. Student gives an unclear or inaccurate explanation on shifting tangent and secant functions.

0 Response is missing or inappropriate.

TASK 4 Scoring Guide:
Check students' work.

3 Student describes a correct process for locating the asymptotes of a tangent function. Student gives clear and accurate descriptions of the relationships between the reciprocal functions.

2 Student has errors in the description of locating the asymptotes of the tangent function. Student gives accurate descriptions of the relationships between the reciprocal functions.

1 Student has errors in the description of locating the asymptotes of the tangent function. Student gives an inaccurate description of the relationships between the reciprocal functions.

0 Response is missing or inappropriate.

Cumulative Review

1. D **2.** C **3.** A **4.** A **5.** C **6.** D **7.** A **8.** B **9.** B **10.** A
11. D **12.** A **13.** C **14.** B **15.** $y = 3x - 35$

16. undefined **17.** ≈ 1.4 cm **18.** $\dfrac{2\sqrt{3}}{3}$

19. Answers may vary. Sample: $\begin{bmatrix} 1 & 0 \\ 2 & 1 \\ 5 & 2 \end{bmatrix}$

20. Shift the graph of $y = \cos x$ to the right $\frac{\pi}{2}$ units and up 1 unit.